THE NOBLE GASES

Other books on chemistry by Isaac Asimov

Biochemistry and Human Metabolism

The Chemicals of Life

Chemistry and Human Health

Inside the Atom

Building Blocks of the Universe

The World of Carbon

The World of Nitrogen

Life and Energy

The Search for the Elements

The Genetic Code

Asimov's Biographical Encyclopedia of Science and Technology

A Short History of Chemistry

The New Intelligent Man's Guide to Science

THE

ISAAC ASIMOV

NOBLE GASES

 Basic Books, Inc., Publishers, *New York*

© 1966 by Isaac Asimov

Library of Congress Catalog Card Number: 66–13510

Manufactured in the United States of America

Designed by Jacqueline Schuman

To Richard DeHaan and Pat Van Doren,
who make book-writing fun

Contents

LIST OF TABLES   *ix*

1 Before the Beginning   *1*

2 Argon   *16*

3 Argon's Family   *28*

4 Noble-Gas Atoms   *47*

5 Noble-Gas Supply   *67*

6 Uses of Noble Gases   *82*

7 Helium   *91*

8 The Inertness of Noble Gases   *113*

9 Fluorine   *131*

10 Noble-Gas Compounds   *145*

SOME NOTABLE DATES IN NOBLE-GAS HISTORY   *162*

INDEX   *165*

LIST OF TABLES

1. Composition of Air (as given in 1890)   *11*
2. Composition of Air (as given in 1894)   *26*
3. The Valence of the Elements in Order of Atomic Weight   *30*
4. Argon's Place in Order of Atomic Weight   *32*
5. Argon's Place in Order of Valence   *33*
6. Portion of the Periodic Table (as given in 1890)   *34*
7. Portion of the Periodic Table (as given in 1894)   *35*
8. Portion of the Periodic Table (as given in July 1898)   *41*
9. Composition of Air (as given now)   *42*
10. Portion of the Periodic Table (as given in 1910)   *46*
11. Portion of the Periodic Table (as given now)   *50*
12. Stable Isotopes of Helium, Neon, and Argon   *54*
13. Stable Isotopes of Krypton and Xenon   *54*
14. Naturally Occurring Isotopes of Radon   *56*
15. Nuclear Structure of Isotopes of Helium, Neon, and Argon   *60*
16. Nuclear Structure of Isotopes of Krypton, Xenon, and Radon   *60*
17. Electron Distribution in the Valence-2 Elements   *63*
18. Electron Distribution in the Valence-1 Elements   *65*
19. Electron Distribution in the Noble Gases   *66*
20. Elemental Abundances in the Universe   *68*
21. Atomic Abundances of the Noble Gases in the Atmosphere   *77*

22. Total Mass of the Stable Noble Gases in
    the Atmosphere   *80*
23. Total Mass of Some Stable Noble-Gas Isotopes in
    the Atmosphere   *81*
24. Densities of Various Gases   *93*
25. Solubilities of Some Common Gases   *98*
26. Solubilities of the Noble Gases   *99*
27. Boiling Points of Some Low-Boiling Gases   *103*
28. Boiling Points of the Noble Gases   *104*
29. Melting Points of Some Gases   *106*
30. Ionization Potentials of the Alkali Metals   *123*
31. Ionization Potentials of the Noble Gases   *125*
32. The Most Electronegative Elements   *129*

THE NOBLE GASES

I

Before the Beginning

Every once in a while, something particularly astonishing and unexpected happens in science. Every once in a while something upsets the apple cart.

A perfect example of such an event came in 1962 when noble-gas compounds were formed for the first time. The whole world of chemistry was thunderstruck.

People outside of chemistry might, of course, feel surprised at all the excitement. Why is it so surprising that noble-gas compounds can be formed? What are noble gases? Why are they called noble?

In this book I shall try to answer these questions, among many others, and, in doing so, a peculiar coincidence will be uncovered. The entire history of the noble gases has consisted of one astonishing and unexpected event after another.

Although the noble gases are quite uncommon and have only a few specialized uses, no other substances in all the world have so dramatic a story behind them.

Some of the drama begins a full century before the noble gases were actually discovered. It begins in the fading years of the eighteenth century, when the great glamour substance in the scientific headlines was nothing more than—air. To consider air, we must go back even further in time.

Van Helmont Meets Chaos

Men have always appreciated the importance of air; until modern times, they have always been in awe of it. After all, it cannot be seen nor felt and seems to have no weight; yet, when in motion in the form of a hurricane blast, it can carry widespread destruction.

It is not surprising, then, that to many ancient peoples, gods and demons seemed to ride the storm blast. Frequently, the words used for air in its various forms came to have more mysterious meanings, too. The Latin word *spiritus*, for instance, which refers to air in the form of the breath, has come to be applied also to supernatural beings. Thus, liquids that evaporate easily and seem to disappear into air are still called spirits, so that one speaks of "spirits of alcohol" and "spirits of turpentine" —but one can also speak of "heavenly spirits."

The German word *Geist* means both breath and supernatural beings, in the same way, and has infiltrated English in the form of "ghost."

The ancient Greek philosophers tried to look at the air in a more matter-of-fact way, but they, too, recognized it as having great importance. They considered it one of the fundamental materials (or *elements*) out of which the universe was made. To these ancients, air was a single substance, and anything that evaporated or fumed, anything that changed into a vapor, mist, or smoke, had simply become air.

The first man to recognize that all forms of air were not necessarily the same substance was a Flemish chemist, Jan Baptista van Helmont (1577–1644). He studied vapors of all sorts, obtained not only when liquids evaporated, but also when he burned wood or charcoal, or allowed grapes to ferment.

The airlike substance he obtained from burning wood interested him particularly; and since it clearly did not behave like ordinary air, he did not wish to call it air. In searching for a new word (according to one story), he harked back to Greek mythology. The Greeks had imagined the universe, in the beginning, to consist of all forms of matter in one grand, disorganized mixture. This primeval, disorganized matter they called "chaos" and out of it the organized universe was formed.

To Van Helmont, the airlike substances seemed to be a bit of chaos left over. They had no form or shape, and different airlike substances mixed easily together into one grand, disorganized mixture. Van Helmont decided to call all such substances by the old name of chaos. He pronounced the word, however, in his native Flemish manner, and spelled it as he pronounced it. For that reason chaos became *gas* and all airlike substances became gases.

Van Helmont called his airlike substance from burning wood *gas sylvestre*, which, translated from Latin into English, means "gas from wood." Using modern chemical terms, we would call that gas *carbon dioxide*. Carbon dioxide, therefore, was the first gas, other than air itself, to be recognized as a distinct substance.

The word gas caught on in some parts of Europe, probably because of its similarity to the German *Geist*. (It is even possible that Van Helmont got the word from *Geist*, rather than from chaos.) In England, however, the term "air" for all kinds of gases persisted for two centuries after Van Helmont.

The Gases of Air

Van Helmont was a century ahead of his time. He had no way of collecting particular gases in order to study them. Any gases that he did form mixed with air and were lost.

The study of gases reached maturity, however, in the eighteenth century. In 1727, an English curate and amateur scientist, Stephen Hales (1677–1761), published a book in which he described his experiments on gases. He devised methods for leading gases, as they formed, through tubes into upended containers of water. The gas bubbled up through the water, forcing it out of the container. Eventually, the container held nothing but the gas, which could then be studied in comfort. Hales was able to describe some properties of gases such as Van Helmont's carbon dioxide. He also studied those gases that we now call hydrogen, carbon monoxide, methane, and sulfur dioxide.

Certain gases are soluble in water. When led into a container of water, they dissolve in the water and disappear. Another English man of God, a Unitarian minister named Joseph Priestley (1733–1804), was the first to lead gases into containers of mercury rather than water. In this way, in the 1770's, he became the first to collect and study water-soluble gases such as those now known as ammonia and hydrogen chloride.

All these gases, however, were special substances formed in the laboratory by chemists. Air itself was still *the* gas, and through most of the eighteenth century was still regarded as an element, that is, as a fundamental building block of the universe that could not be separated into any still simpler substance.*

---

* For a discussion of the chemical elements and how they came to be discovered, see Isaac Asimov, *Search for the Elements* (New York: Basic Books, 1962).

Air might carry solid and liquid matter, of course: dust, soot, water droplets. It might also contain vapors of water and other volatile liquids. Yet if one dealt with filtered, cooled, dry air from which all these impurities were removed, what was left was the true air itself; this residue was considered the element.

The first blow to this view (though a small one) came in the 1750's, when a Scottish chemist, Joseph Black (1728–1799), studied carbon dioxide carefully. Among other things, he discovered that when this gas was passed over a white solid substance we now call calcium oxide, that substance turned crumbly and became calcium carbonate.

Furthermore, Black discovered that if calcium oxide were merely exposed to air, it underwent the same change. Slowly, perhaps, but very surely. To him, this seemed to indicate that ordinary air contained small amounts of carbon dioxide. Yet the amount of carbon dioxide present was barely measurable; it could be considered as just another impurity. The large bulk of the air still seemed a simple substance.

The real breakthrough came with exploration of the facts of combustion? When a candle was burned in a closed container of air, it soon went out. The candle did not, however, use up the air. In fact, it used up only a comparatively small portion of it. Why, then, did it go out?

Black assigned that problem to a student of his, the Scottish chemist Daniel Rutherford (1749–1819). Rutherford isolated the portion of the air that was not consumed by the burning candle and found that nothing would burn in it. Nor could mice live in it. This was also true for carbon dioxide, but the unconsumed portion of the air did not have the properties of carbon dioxide. It would not convert calcium oxide to calcium carbonate, for instance.

In 1772, Rutherford reported his investigations of the gas in which candles would not burn. He based his conclusions on the "phlogiston theory." In the eighteenth century, chemists believed that a burning substance gave off phlogiston to the air and that it was only by giving off phlogiston that it could continue to burn. Rutherford decided, therefore, that his gas was simply air that had absorbed all the phlogiston it could hold, and so he called it "phlogisticated air." Since it had all the phlogiston it could hold, it would accept no more, and nothing would burn in it.

Meanwhile, Priestley was tackling air from another angle. He heated mercury until some of it combined with air to form a brick-red, powdery substance, which we now call "mercuric oxide." Priestley skimmed off this combination of mercury and air, placed it in a glass container, and heated it by means of a large lens that focused sunlight upon it. The mercury/air combination broke up; droplets of liquid mercury appeared on the inner glass surface, and air was given off. This air was not quite like ordinary air, however. Objects burned furiously in it; smoldering splints burst into open flame.

Priestley's gas was the opposite of Rutherford's gas, it seemed. Priestley's gas appeared to be unusually low in phlogiston; consequently, it accepted more phlogiston with unusual readiness and objects burned in it eagerly. When Priestley reported his findings in 1774, he called the gas "dephlogisticated air."

Priestley's work came to the attention of a French chemist, Antoine-Laurent Lavoisier (1743–1794), who later came to be considered the "Father of Modern Chemistry." It was Lavoisier, who, with several others, eventually introduced modern chemical terminology, so that we speak of carbon dioxide instead of *gas sylvestre* and copper sulfate instead of "blue vitriol." It was Lavoisier's use of Van Helmont's term "gas" that finally established its use in the chemical vocabulary.

Lavoisier had been studying the manner in which some substances burned and others rusted. He found that, in either case, only part of the air was consumed. In the light of Priestley's findings, Lavoisier came to the conclusion that instead of worrying about phlogiston, matters could be explained more easily by supposing that air was not an element but was a mixture of at least two gases, both of which were probably elements.

One of these gases, Lavoisier suggested, could support combustion. Flammable objects would burn in its presence and combine with it in the process. Lavoisier called this gas *oxygen*, from Greek words meaning "producing sourness," because he thought it was essential to the structure of all sour substances (acids). In this, he proved to be wrong, but the name has persisted.

The other gas could not support combustion. In its presence, candles went out and mice died. Lavoisier named it "azote" from Greek words meaning "no life," but the alternate name *nitrogen* ("producing niter") was later adopted because the gas was essential to the structure of the common mineral niter.

Because of Priestley's studies of his "dephlogisticated air," he is now accepted as the discoverer of oxygen. Rutherford's work on "phlogisticated air" makes him the discoverer of nitrogen. However, Lavoisier's analysis of the situation was more important than either discovery in itself. As a result of Lavoisier's work, it became clear that filtered dry air had a composition of about one-fifth oxygen and four-fifths nitrogen, with no other gas present in more than tiny amounts.

Cavendish's Bubble

This was the situation with respect to the study of air when an English chemist, Henry Cavendish (1731–1810), took a hand. He was already interested in gases, for in 1766 he had reported in some detail on the properties of an unusual gas he had obtained by allowing acids to react with metals. The gas in question was extremely flammable and unusually light; later, Cavendish discovered that when this gas burned, it formed water. Lavoisier, on hearing this, promptly named the gas *hydrogen* ("producing water"). Hydrogen had been produced long before Cavendish; both Van Helmont and Hales had worked with it. Cavendish's studies were the first, however, to be systematic and detailed, and he is usually given credit for discovering the gas.

In 1785, Cavendish experimented directly with air. From the course of his work, we might suspect that he was not satisfied that air consisted of only two gases, oxygen and nitrogen. The evidence was insufficient.

We can reason it out as follows: The presence of oxygen seems a certainty because oxygen does something—for instance, it combines with the substance of burning candles. The gas left over after the oxygen disappeared was given a name only because it did nothing. How could one be certain that there was only one substance in the air that did nothing? What if there were two, three, four, or any number of gases that were completely different except that none of them would support combustion?

After all, carbon dioxide doesn't support combustion and neither does water vapor. If carbon dioxide and water vapor were mixed with nitrogen, the mixture would not support combustion. If a candle were thrust into the mixture, it would promptly go out. Mice penned up in such a mixture would die. Yet all this would not be sufficient grounds for deciding that the mixture was pure nitrogen.

Each of the components of such a mixture would have to be identified by some positive characteristic. For instance, if the mixture were cooled to below the freezing point of water, most of the water vapor would settle out as frost. If what was left were bubbled through water, most of the carbon dioxide would dissolve. What was left—impervious to ordinary cold, insoluble in water—would be nitrogen. But would it? Can we be certain that there are not other gases that will not support combustion and that are also unaffected by cold and water?

If this were Cavendish's reasoning, then it would be necessary for him to find something that nitrogen would do, and see if all the gas that was called nitrogen would indeed do it.

For the purpose, Cavendish made use of electricity. In the eighteenth century, the electric current, now so familiar to us, was not known, but static electricity devices were popular. In such devices, a static electrical charge could be produced by friction and stored. When the stored charge grew sufficiently strong, it could be made to spark across a small air gap. When this electric spark flashed through the air, the nitrogen and oxygen in its neighborhood were forced into combination, forming compounds that were soluble in water, although nitrogen and oxygen, individually, were not.

Here was something that could have significant results. If electric sparks were passed through air in a closed container and the air bubbled through water, some of the nitrogen and oxygen would be removed. Eventually, all the nitrogen and oxygen would be removed in the form of water-soluble compounds; any gas remaining would be neither nitrogen nor oxygen.

To be sure, if Cavendish had started only with pure air, his electric spark would have ceased being effective after only a quarter of the air was gone. But, then, air to begin with is only one-fifth oxygen. This oxygen combines with approximately half its weight of nitrogen, so that by the time a quarter of the air is gone there is no oxygen left.

Cavendish therefore added additional pure oxygen to air, until he had a gas mixture composed of five parts of oxygen to three parts of nitrogen. Under these conditions, almost every bit of the air was forced into water-soluble combination. It seemed that the gas called nitrogen was indeed nitrogen all the way.

But wait! Here comes the first item of drama. A small

bubble of gas remained that did not combine with oxygen! Cavendish added quite a bit of oxygen to it, sparked and sparked away, then removed the oxygen, and found the remaining bit of gas untouched. He continued the sparking for weeks without any visible effect on that final bubble.

That last bit of gas, which behaved like neither oxygen nor nitrogen, made up about 1/120 of the original sample of air, according to Cavendish's calculations. From this, one could conclude that about 99 per cent of the portion of the air supposed to be nitrogen really was nitrogen.

But that last bit had to be a different gas and one with rather unusual properties. Nitrogen was difficult enough to force into combination with oxygen. Heat alone, for instance, wouldn't do it (and luckily so, or the atmosphere would go up in flames the first time we struck a match). An electric spark would indeed force nitrogen and oxygen together, but only in the immediate neighborhood and only while the spark was in existence. As soon as the spark ceased, combination ceased. (Were it not for that, the atmosphere would go up in flames at the first lightning bolt, for lightning is merely a gigantic electric spark.)

Nitrogen, in other words, is an inert gas, because its refusal to combine with other substances except under extreme conditions can be looked upon as the result of inertia, or a kind of laziness.

Cavendish's gas was, however, much more inert than nitrogen. In fact, it seemed completely inert; and at that time, nothing like it was known in chemistry.

Perhaps the very strangeness of such a completely inert gas (a "noble gas," as it is now called) rather embarrassed chemists, who tended to look the other way. No one followed up Cavendish's report, and it seems to have slipped out of the chemical consciousness for a little over a hundred years.

Chemists worked out the composition of the air in more and more delicate fashion, but they assumed that whatever was not oxygen was nitrogen. By 1890 there seemed no doubt whatever that the composition of pure air was that given in Table 1.

Table 1. Composition of Air (as given in 1890)

Gas	Per Cent by Volume
Nitrogen	79
Oxygen	21
Carbon dioxide	0.04

Lines of Light

Cavendish's discovery of a noble gas failed to take root, and as though that weren't disappointing enough (now that we look back on it), a second discovery missed fire seventy years later.

The second discovery was quite different from that of Cavendish. It involved light rather than electricity, and was not a chemical affair at all. It could, rather, be considered part of the history of astronomy.

This new account really begins with the English scientist Isaac Newton (1642–1727), who, in 1665, found that if a shaft of sunlight were allowed to pass through a triangular piece of glass (a "prism") it would spread out into a band of colors. Newton called this band of colors a *spectrum*, a Latin word that was used for any "ghostly apparition," for the colors appeared where none had been visible before and seemed to be seen but not felt, like so many ghosts. (The same succession of colors appears in the rainbow; indeed, the rainbow is a naturally occurring spectrum formed when sunlight passes through tiny water droplets that fill the air immediately after a rain.)

It at once became clear that this discovery was of the highest importance in the investigation of light. For nearly two centuries, however, no one suspected that it would also be of crucial importance to the science of chemistry.

In 1814, the first step in that direction was taken by a

German optician, Joseph von Fraunhofer (1787–1826). He was studying the fine glass he used to make his instruments, and was testing its effect on a beam of sunlight that emerged from a narrow slit and then passed through a prism. Fraunhofer found that the spectra which were formed were crossed by numerous dark lines. He measured the position of several hundred of these lines and lettered the most prominent ones from A to K. They are still sometimes called "Fraunhofer lines" in his honor.

In succeeding decades, scientists studied these lines more and more curiously. The climax came with the work of the German physicist Gustav Robert Kirchhoff (1824–1887). He was able to show that when elements were heated to the point where they gave off light, and that light was passed through a prism, it was divided into a pattern of bright lines of various colors against a dark background. Under other conditions, an element could be made to produce an identical pattern of dark lines against a backdrop of continuous color.

Kirchhoff, working with the German chemist Robert Wilhelm von Bunsen (1811–1899), constructed a *spectroscope*, a device by which he could produce the lines and measure their position. He showed that each element produced a specific pattern of lines like that of no other element. Indeed, no element produced even a single line that was exactly in the same position as a particular line produced by another element. (It was as though each element produced its own "fingerprint" of light.)

If a mineral were heated to the point where it glowed, the various lines it produced were sufficient to indicate the nature of the elements present. By 1859, Kirchhoff and Bunsen had established a new chemical technique, *spectroscopic analysis*.

Consequently, if a heated mineral produced one or more spectral lines appearing in new positions that did not duplicate the positions of the lines of any known elements, there were strong grounds for suspicion of the existence of a new element. In 1860, Kirchhoff and Bunsen located new lines in the spectrum formed by heating a certain mineral; they deduced the presence of a new element. They named it *cesium* from a Latin word meaning "sky blue" because of the color of the new line. The next year they discovered another element in the same way, *rubidium* ("red," again from the color of the new line).

Two other elements were discovered by the same method in the next few years: *thallium* ("green twig") by the English physicist William Crookes (1832–1919) in 1861, and *indium* ("indigo") by a pair of German mineralogists, Ferdinand Reich (1799–1882) and Hieronymus Theodor Richter (1824–1898), in 1863.

In every case, once the new element was pointed out, the mineral could be tackled by ordinary chemical procedures, and the resultant element was isolated and studied. Almost at once, therefore, spectroscopy gained enormous prestige.

It seemed evident that the dark lines Fraunhofer had observed in the spectrum of sunlight must be produced by elements in the sun. A Swedish astronomer, Anders Jonas Ångström (1814–1874), studied the solar spectrum carefully in 1861 and showed that some of its lines were in positions identical with those produced by glowing hydrogen. It could be concluded, then, that hydrogen was present in the sun. An English astronomer, William Huggins (1824–1910), studied the spectra produced by astronomical bodies other than the sun and showed that specific elements could be located there.

Spectroscopic analysis was rapidly progressing from triumph to triumph and was setting the stage for the dramatic event of 1868. In that year, a total eclipse was going to be visible in India and astronomers traveled there from all over the world. During eclipses, it is possible to study objects on the sun's surface, such as spurts of flaming gas called "prominences," as well as the sun's corona, its thin outer atmosphere.

Ordinarily, when the sun's bright disk is not obscured by the moon, such comparatively faint detail as the prominences and the corona are completely drowned out.

One of the astronomers reaching India was a Frenchman, Pierre Jules César Janssen (1824–1907). He brought with him a spectroscope, which he intended to use in his observations. Janssen let the light from the outer part of the sun pass through the spectroscope so that bright lines were formed. He recorded their position and found one that, so far as he knew, was in a position that did not belong to any of the lines of any known element.

He did not consider himself sufficiently expert in spectroscopic analysis to carry the matter further; indeed, he did not even mention the new line in his final report on the eclipse. However, he did send the data to an English astronomer, Joseph Norman Lockyer (1836–1920), who was doing considerable work in spectroscopy.

Lockyer considered the matter, studied solar spectra for himself, and found the line. Nor could he duplicate it with any known element. Lockyer decided that a new element was involved—one that was present in the sun but that was, as yet, unknown on earth. He suggested that the new element be named *helium*, from the Greek word for "sun."

Lockyer's suggestion was shrugged off by the world of chemistry. Spectroscopic analysis could discover new elements, yes, but chemists felt they had to confirm the discoveries by orthodox analysis. They were not yet ready to accept spectroscopic evidence as sufficient in itself, without chemical confirmation, for the existence of an element in the heavens that was not known on earth.

Consequently, the matter was forgotten until nearly the end of the century. For a generation, no one suspected that the "Janssen-Lockyer line" was the second time that the existence of the noble gases had actually been detected.

The Trapped Gas

As the nineteenth century waned, two discoveries of the noble gases had been made, recorded, and ignored. A third case misfired even more badly.

An American mineralogist, William Francis Hillebrand (1853–1925), was treating a mineral with acid, a routine procedure. The mineral was *uraninite* (more commonly known as "pitchblende"), which is rich in the heavy metal, uranium.

Hillebrand found that under this treatment, small quantities of gas bubbled off. This is not surprising, for minerals, when forming, often trap tiny bubbles of gas in their solidifying substance. Such minerals are said to contain *occluded gas*.

The gas Hillebrand obtained was not soluble in water, did not react with oxygen when heated, was colorless, odorless, and tasteless. In those days, a colorless, odorless, tasteless, inert gas meant only one thing—nitrogen. That was a reasonable conclusion, since nitrogen was always present in the air and therefore always available for occlusion by minerals as they formed.

Hillebrand studied the spectrum of the gas; sure enough, he found lines representing nitrogen. That certainly seemed to settle the matter, and Hillebrand therefore published his results in 1890, and reported the presence of occluded nitrogen in uraninite.

But there had been other lines in the spectrum of the gas; those lines Hillebrand referred to, but did not identify. In fact, he could not identify them, but, for some reason, he decided to go no further. In making that decision, he lost his chance at great fame. Like Cavendish, he actually had a sample of noble gas in his hand. (For the moment, I shall refer to this as "Hillebrand's gas.")

2

Argon

Prout's Hypothesis

With two disregarded hits and one miss, we can now pass on to the discovery that finally made itself felt. It came about through a line of research that no one could possibly have suspected would yield the results it did. It was a classic case of scientists looking for one thing and unexpectedly finding another of much more startling nature.*

The line of research began with the English chemist John Dalton (1766–1844), who, in 1803, first advanced his *atomic*

---

* This procedure is now called "serendipity" from Serendib, an old name for the island of Ceylon. It owes its name to a story entitled *The Three Princes of Serendib*, written by the eighteenth-century English writer, Horace Walpole, in which the three princes kept finding, through accident, objects more valuable than those for which they were searching.

theory, which involved the suggestion that all matter consisted of tiny *atoms.* All the atoms of a given element were alike, according to this theory, but the atoms of any one element were different from those of all others.

The distinguishing characteristic of the different kinds of atoms, Dalton felt, was their weight; he was the first who tried to work out what the *atomic weights* of the different elements might be.

There was no available technique at that time (or for a century afterward) by which the actual weight of an individual atom might be measured, but the relative weights could be determined. That is, if an arbitrary number were assigned to the atom of some element, it would then be possible to tell whether the atom of another element were half as heavy, or twice as heavy, and an arbitrary number could be assigned to it as well.

For instance, the custom arose of assigning the number 16 to the oxygen atom, so that one could say that the atomic weight of oxygen was 16. It turned out that the hydrogen atom had a weight of roughly 1/16 that of the oxygen atom, so that hydrogen could be assigned the atomic weight of 1. The carbon atom had a weight 3/4 that of the oxygen atom; therefore, carbon could be assigned the atomic weight of 12. In the same way one could determine that nitrogen had an atomic weight of 14; sulfur, 32; sodium, 23, and so on.

The first lists produced by Dalton made it appear that all the atomic weights were whole numbers. This seemed more than one could expect of coincidence. In 1815, an anonymous article appeared which suggested that all atoms were built up of hydrogen. Since hydrogen had an atomic weight of 1, all the other atomic weights had to be integers. The anonymous author proved to be the English physician William Prout (1785–1850), and the suggestion came to be called *Prout's hypothesis.*

This was an attractive suggestion, for it reduced the universe to a single substance—hydrogen. Everything else was made up of combinations of that one basic substance. Scientists and philosophers had been searching for evidence for such a belief ever since ancient Greek times nearly 2,500 years before. Could the evidence now really exist? In order for Prout's hypothesis to be true, all the atomic weights would need to be integers. As further data were accumulated, this proved not to be so.

In 1828, the Swedish chemist Jöns Jakob Berzelius (1779–1848) published a list of atomic weights that was the result of more painstaking and thorough work than Dalton's had been. Quite a few elements proved to have atomic weights that were not whole numbers. To use examples from modern tables, chlorine has an atomic weight of about 35.5, boron has one of about 10.8, copper of about 63.5, magnesium of about 24.3, and so on. Berzelius, it certainly seemed, had disproved the validity of Prout's hypothesis.

Yet chemists had nagging doubts. It is not easy to determine atomic weights. The chemist must work with completely pure material. He must bring about chemical reactions in such a way that he knows exactly what chemical changes are taking place. He must weigh the various elements taking part in those changes, and the compounds that are formed, with great accuracy. Small errors creeping in here or there might make a drastic difference to the atomic weight.

All through the nineteenth century, therefore, chemists attempted to determine and redetermine atomic weights with the greatest possible accuracy in order to see whether Prout's hypothesis was truly valid or not. Throughout the nineteenth century, the results seemed to confirm Berzelius' work more and more completely. Prout's hypothesis was killed a dozen times.

In 1882, John William Strutt, the third Baron Rayleigh (1842–1919), usually referred to as Lord Rayleigh, undertook to tackle the problem once again. He worked with those elements that, under ordinary conditions, existed as gases: in particular, oxygen, hydrogen, and nitrogen.

By then, chemists had good reason to believe that the density of these gases was in direct proportion to their atomic weight. In other words, if it were true that the atomic weights of hydrogen, nitrogen, and oxygen were exactly 1, 14, and 16, respectively, then the density of nitrogen ought to be just 14 times greater than that of hydrogen, and the density of oxygen ought to be just 16 times greater than that of hydrogen.

Put this way, it sounds simple; but, in actual practice, measuring the density of gases accurately enough to determine the atomic weights can be quite difficult. Rayleigh kept at this sort of work, on and off, for fully ten years, before he could report with confidence, in 1892, that the density of oxygen was not quite 16 times greater than that of hydrogen. It was only 15.882 times greater.

This meant that if the oxygen atom were given an atomic weight of 16, the hydrogen atom would have to be given one of 1.007, since $16/15.882 = 1.007$.

It also meant that if the oxygen atom were built up of hydrogen atoms, it would have to be built up of 15.882 hydrogen atoms. In 1892, chemists were still convinced that it was impossible for atoms to be broken up into fractions. Oxygen atoms might be made up of 15 hydrogen atoms, or 16, but never of 15.882 hydrogen atoms.

Once again, Prout's hypothesis seemed to stand disproved.

Rayleigh's Puzzle

But this did not represent all of Rayleigh's work. He also measured the density of nitrogen, and, but for one snag, could have reported that its density was slightly less than 14 times that of hydrogen, so that nitrogen atoms could not be built up out of hydrogen atoms any more than oxygen atoms could.

The snag that halted him revolved about the purity of the nitrogen he used. Rayleigh, in measuring his densities, made use of samples of gas that he prepared in different ways. He reasoned that when he prepared a gas it might contain an impurity with a particular density of its own that would slightly change the over-all density of the gas. This impurity would arise because of the particular method of preparation. If he prepared the same gas in three different ways, there might be three different impurities, and three different over-all densities. On the other hand, if the same gas, prepared in several different ways, always had precisely the same density, that was strong evidence in favor of the presumption that no perceptible traces of impurity were present.

In the cases of oxygen and hydrogen, Rayleigh had no trouble. Hydrogen, carefully prepared in a number of ways, always gave the same density measurement, and this was true of oxygen, too.

Not so, however, with nitrogen. Rayleigh had obtained nitrogen, in one case, from dry, filtered air from which oxygen had been removed by passage over red-hot copper. All the oxygen combined with the copper while the nitrogen, untouched, passed on. We can call this gas "atmosphere-nitrogen."

He had also prepared nitrogen in this fashion, after adding a quantity of ammonia to the air. Ammonia is a gas made up of a combination of nitrogen and hydrogen. In the presence of red-hot copper, the hydrogen atoms in the ammonia are removed along with the oxygen from the air, and the nitrogen that results comes partly from the air and partly from the ammonia. Let us refer to this as the "ammonia-nitrogen," even though it is partly from the air, too.

It would seem that the atmosphere-nitrogen and the ammonia-nitrogen ought to have the same density. After all, nitrogen is nitrogen.

Yet Rayleigh's careful measurements showed that the ammonia-nitrogen was distinctly less dense than the atmosphere-nitrogen—almost 0.1 per cent less dense.

A discrepancy of but 0.1 per cent is not much, but it was far too great for Rayleigh to ignore. The care with which he made his measurements was such that a discrepancy of this size would not be expected to appear; it did not appear in the case of hydrogen and oxygen. Still, no matter how often he repeated his work, Rayleigh always obtained the same results: the ammonia-nitrogen was distinctly less dense than the atmosphere-nitrogen.

Rayleigh thought of four possible explanations.

First: Could it be that the atmosphere-nitrogen still contained some oxygen? Oxygen is somewhat denser than nitrogen and its presence would raise the density figure for atmosphere-nitrogen. But oxygen was only slightly denser than nitrogen; to raise the density figure by 0.1 per cent, there would have to be considerable oxygen present, nearly 1 per cent of the total gas. That would certainly be enough to be detected easily, and to be removed, too. Yet no oxygen impurity could be detected. Scratch possibility one!

Second: Could it be that the ammonia-nitrogen still contained some hydrogen? Hydrogen was less dense than nitrogen and would therefore, if present, lower the density figure for ammonia-nitrogen. What is more, hydrogen was considerably less dense than nitrogen and it would not take very much to lower the figures by the required amount. Even so, the required amount was too great. Hydrogen could easily be detected and removed even in the small quantities required to explain the discrepancy, and it was not detected. It simply was not present. Scratch possibility two.

The third possibility requires a little preliminary explanation. The gases (nitrogen, hydrogen, and oxygen) do not consist of single, separated atoms. The atoms of these gases have a strong tendency to combine with other kinds of atoms; if no other kinds of atoms are present, they will combine among themselves.

Atom combinations are called *molecules*. Since hydrogen atoms combine in pairs, gaseous hydrogen is actually made up of *hydrogen molecules,* each made up of a pair of hydrogen atoms. In the same way, oxygen and nitrogen consist of *oxygen molecules* and of *nitrogen molecules,* with both sets of molecules made up of pairs of atoms.

It is customary for chemists to symbolize atoms of the elements hydrogen, oxygen, and nitrogen by their initial letters H, O, and N, respectively. The respective molecules, made up of two atoms each, are symbolized as H_2, O_2, and N_2.

It so happens that, under certain conditions, oxygen atoms can be put together three at a time, to form a molecule symbolized as O_3. Such molecules compose the gas *ozone,* which, as you see, is a form of oxygen.

Ozone contains a higher energy content than ordinary oxygen does; left to itself, it tends to break up into ordinary oxygen again. To force that third atom into the molecule is difficult. One way of doing so is to make use of electric sparks passing through the oxygen. The electrical energy forces three oxygen atoms together in the same way as, for Cavendish, it forced nitrogen atoms and oxygen atoms together.

Now consider ozone (O_3) and ordinary oxygen (O_2). Chemists have good reason to believe that the same number of molecules fit into the same volume in the case of both gases (indeed, in the case of all gases), under equivalent conditions of temperature and pressure. However, the ozone molecules contain half again as many atoms as do the oxygen molecules. For every 100 oxygen atoms in a particular volume of oxygen (50 O_2 molecules) there are 150 oxygen atoms in the same volume of ozone (50 O_3 molecules). Consequently, the density of ozone ought to be half again as great as that of oxygen and, on measurement, this proves indeed to be the case.

We are now ready for Rayleigh's third possibility.

Third: What if nitrogen, too, forms three-atom molecules (N_3) and if some N_3 was present in atmosphere-nitrogen but not in ammonia-nitrogen. Since N_3 could be expected to be half again as dense as N_2, could not its presence raise the density of atmosphere-nitrogen by the necessary amount?

But why should N_3 appear only in atmosphere-nitrogen and not in ammonia-nitrogen? There seemed no reasonable explanation for that, and there was no use merely substituting one puzzle for another. Then, too, there were good reasons to suppose that N_3 would be no more stable than O_3; in fact, almost surely less stable. That means that N_3 ought to break down to N_2 on standing, and quite quickly, and that the density of atmosphere-nitrogen ought to decrease with time. But this did not happen!

Rayleigh also tackled this problem from another angle. Passing electric discharges through nitrogen ought to form N_3, if such a gas existed, just as passing them through oxygen formed O_3. The density of nitrogen ought to increase as electric sparks were passed through it for longer and longer times. But it did not!

Rayleigh decided that there was no evidence for the existence of N_3 at all, let alone in the atmosphere-nitrogen. Scratch possibility three.

Fourth: Could it be that some of the nitrogen molecules in the ammonia-nitrogen broke down to *atomic nitrogen*: nitrogen, that is, that consisted of single nitrogen atoms; and that this did not happen in the atmosphere-nitrogen. A collection of atomic nitrogen (N) would naturally be only half as dense as ordinary nitrogen (N_2) and if present in small quantities in ammonia-nitrogen could easily lower its density by the necessary amount.

But why should nitrogen molecules break up into atomic nitrogen in ammonia-nitrogen and not in atmosphere-nitrogen? It was known that single nitrogen atoms simply did not exist as such for any length of time. They quickly joined to form nitrogen molecules. This meant that the density of ammonia-nitrogen ought to rise with time, but it did not. Scratch possibility four.

While Rayleigh was eliminating all the escape hatches, he succeeded in making the discrepancy worse, but narrowed the nature of the problem.

Remember that what I am calling ammonia-nitrogen was prepared from ammonia mixed with air. What, thought Rayleigh, if he made use of ammonia only? He would then get "pure-ammonia-nitrogen" and completely leave out any contaminating more-dense atmosphere-nitrogen. Would not this make the discrepancy in density greater?

It did just that. When he prepared pure-ammonia-nitrogen, he found its density to be almost 0.5 per cent less than that of atmosphere-nitrogen. Almost half a per cent! Insupportable!

Rayleigh then went on to prepare nitrogen from various chemicals and found that nitrogen so prepared always had just about the density of pure-ammonia-nitrogen.

Only atmosphere-nitrogen stood out from the rest. It was distinctly denser than any form of nitrogen prepared from any substance other than the atmosphere. Rayleigh was sure, then, that the explanation, whatever it was, lay in the atmosphere. But that did not help him get any closer to the solution.

Ramsay's Answer

Rayleigh was almost beside himself with frustration and felt he had come to a dead end. Perhaps what was needed was a fresh approach; the thoughts of some man who had not gone stale through long, drawn-out concentration on the problem.

Even while he was still conducting his experiments, he had published a letter in the September 29, 1892, issue of the British scientific journal *Nature*. In this letter, he stated the situation in detail, and asked for suggestions. None were received.

In 1893, however, Rayleigh received a communication from a Scottish chemist, William Ramsay (1852–1916). Ramsay was interested in the subject, had been in communication with Rayleigh on the matter earlier, and now specifically requested Rayleigh's permission to follow up some ideas of his own on the question of the density of nitrogen. Rayleigh gave his permission gladly.

Ramsay reasoned that since the trouble lay in the atmosphere-nitrogen, there must be some impurity in it that was denser than nitrogen itself and that ought to differ in its chemical properties.

Molecular nitrogen, although quite inert, will react with red-hot magnesium to form magnesium nitride. The impurity may also enter into combination with the magnesium; but if so, it will almost surely do so either more readily or less readily than nitrogen. If the impurity combined more readily than nitrogen did, then the atmosphere-nitrogen would be drained of the impurity, and the density of that portion of it that had not yet reacted would drop to the proper value shown by pure-ammonia-nitrogen.

If, on the other hand, the dense impurity reacted with magnesium more slowly than nitrogen did, it would accumulate in the nitrogen that had not yet reacted and the density of what was left would rise ever higher.

With this in mind, Ramsay passed a large volume of atmosphere-nitrogen over red-hot magnesium. When he had only a small quantity of gas left, he measured its density and found it to be fully 7 per cent (!) higher than that of pure-ammonia-nitrogen. The impurity, whatever it was, was reacting with red-hot magnesium less readily than nitrogen was.

This was rather remarkable. Nitrogen was the least active gas known at that time; but here was a gas that seemed even less active.

It reminded Ramsay of Cavendish's old experiment of over a century before (see Page 10). Cavendish had isolated a small quantity of impurity from atmosphere-nitrogen under conditions that indicated that the impurity was even less active than nitrogen.

Ramsay decided to repeat that experiment. He made use of electric sparks to combine nitrogen and oxygen, and he, too, like Cavendish, ended up with a small final bubble that would not combine with oxygen. Cavendish proved to have been dead right. Ramsay even ended with almost the same quantity of impurity.

Ramsay went a step further than Cavendish by determining the density of the impurity. It was some 40 per cent denser than nitrogen. Then, to clear up lingering doubts, Ramsay made use of an instrument unavailable to Cavendish. He heated the gas and studied its light under the spectroscope. Its lines appeared in positions like those of no known element and, in particular, were nothing like the nitrogen lines.

In May 1894, Ramsay wrote to Rayleigh, informing him of the details of his work. Rayleigh confirmed the results by repeating the experiments, and in August 1894, they joined forces to announce the discovery of a new element.

Table 2. *Composition of Air (as given in 1894)*

Gas	Per Cent by Volume
Nitrogen	78
Oxygen	21
Argon	1
Carbon dioxide	0.04

Because the new element seemed completely inert and could not, so far as they could tell, combine with any substance, they called it *argon*, from a Greek word, meaning "inert." The older notions of the composition of the atmosphere had to be revised, of course (see Table 2).

Rayleigh's puzzle was solved completely. When nitrogen

is prepared from the air by simply removing the oxygen, the argon remains and its greater density raises the over-all density of the mixture. On the other hand, since argon does not combine with other substances, nitrogen compounds, however formed, do not contain argon. Therefore, when molecular nitrogen is formed from any nitrogen compound, only nitrogen is obtained and no argon. Pure-ammonia-nitrogen therefore has the true density of nitrogen, half a per cent lower than that of the argon-contaminated atmosphere-nitrogen.

3

Argon's Family

Mendeléev's Table

It is perfectly clear, then, that Cavendish's gas was argon, and that Cavendish had a sample of argon in his grasp over a century before its formal discovery. Looking back with the 20-20 vision of hindsight, it seems a shame that Cavendish's discovery was ignored. On the other hand, the loss to science was not so great as it might have been.

Very often, when a scientific discovery is ignored, it is because it is ahead of its time. By this I mean that other aspects of science have not yet advanced to the point where the discovery can be properly exploited. Scientists, not knowing what to do with a finding that seems a dead end, tend to turn to other discoveries that they can develop and exploit properly.

If chemists generally had recognized the fact that Cavendish had discovered a new inert gas, they would have had the knowledge of the gas, but nothing more. The state of chemistry in 1785 was not such as to allow them to go further. It would not even have allowed them to prepare the new gas in quantity.

By 1894, however, a new view of the elements had been developed that pointed the way to logical additional steps and discoveries. Argon was of such importance to the chemical theories of 1894 that its discovery was followed up eagerly and profitably—as would not have been possible in 1785.

The proper exploitation of the discovery of argon had been made possible as a result of the work of a Russian chemist, Dmitri Ivanovich Mendeléev (1834–1907).

In 1869, he had brought order to the list of elements. He had shown that if the elements were listed in tabular form in the order of molecular weight, certain properties would be found to vary in a regular, periodic fashion, and similar elements would fall in columns in the table. The arrangement has come to be called the *periodic table* of the elements.

One of these regularly varying properties is *valence*, a term used to represent the combining power of different types of atoms. (In fact, "valence" is from a Latin word meaning "power.") Thus, an atom of the element sodium never combines with more than one other atom of any kind. The valence of sodium is therefore taken as 1. An atom of calcium combines with as many as two other atoms, an atom of aluminum with as many as three, an atom of tin with as many as four. Therefore, the valence of calcium is 2, that of aluminum is 3, and that of tin is 4.

Suppose, now, that we list the elements known in 1894 in order of atomic weight and include the valence of each. To avoid certain complications that arise when atomic weights reach values higher than 45, I shall list only the first eighteen elements. That will be enough to make the point (see Table 3).

As you see, the value of the valence moves up and down in

a very neat rhythm that seems to leave no gaps. How can a new element be fitted into such a list without upsetting the rhythm? (Before 1869, new elements were received into the fold without such disturbing questions, but after 1869 such questions had to be asked.)

One thought arose at once. Since argon seemed completely inert, its atoms combined with no others, and could be given a valence of 0. An element with a valence of 0 could then be fitted into the scheme between neighboring elements with valences of 1. The regular scheme of valence would then no longer be 4, 3, 2, 1, 1, 2, 3, 4 but would be 4, 3, 2, 1, 0, 1, 2, 3, 4. The rhythm was not upset at all; in fact, it was improved.

Where in the list, however, could argon be entered? In the

Table 3. The Valence of the Elements in Order of Atomic Weight

Element	Approximate Atomic Weight	Valence
Hydrogen	1.0	1
Lithium	6.9	1
Beryllium	9.0	2
Boron	10.8	3
Carbon	12.0	4
Nitrogen	14.0	3
Oxygen	16.0	2
Fluorine	19.0	1
Sodium	23.0	1
Magnesium	24.3	2
Aluminum	27.0	3
Silicon	28.1	4
Phosphorus	31.0	3
Sulfur	32.1	2
Chlorine	35.5	1
Potassium	39.1	1
Calcium	40.1	2
Scandium	45.0	3

short list of eighteen elements given in Table 3 there are three pairs of neighboring elements with valences of 1: hydrogen-lithium, fluorine-sodium, and chlorine-potassium. Others appear later in the complete list of elements. Between which of these pairs could argon be expected to belong?

We could be guided by argon's atomic weight, which can be determined from its density. The density of argon is about 1.425 times as great as that of nitrogen. Therefore, the argon molecule must weigh 1.425 times as much as the nitrogen molecule. We know that nitrogen consists of two nitrogen atoms; what we need to know next is how many argon atoms are found in the argon molecule.

It turned out that the argon "molecule" consisted of a single atom. Argon was a *monatomic gas*. This was another surprise for chemists. The other gaseous elements—hydrogen, nitrogen, oxygen, fluorine, and chlorine—were all *diatomic gases,* with molecules made up of two atoms each. Argon was the first exception. Apparently, its atoms were so inert they did not even combine among themselves. (Nitrogen atoms are quite active and combine with each other rapidly. It is the combination, N_2, that is inert—and even then not so inert as argon.)

Chemists convinced themselves of the monatomic nature of argon by measuring the heat it would absorb. When heat is added to a diatomic gas, the energy it absorbs shows up in two ways. Individual molecules move in straight lines more quickly and also tumble end-over-end (like tiny dumbbells) more quickly. A monatomic gas can absorb heat only by having its atoms move more quickly in a straight line. The single atoms, being spherical and not dumbbell-shaped, cannot absorb energy by increasing the rate of tumbling. A monatomic gas therefore absorbs less heat for a given temperature rise than a diatomic gas does. When argon was tested in this manner, it absorbed the amount of heat one would expect if it consisted of single atoms. That matter was therefore considered settled.

In a given volume of argon gas there are as many argon atoms as there are nitrogen molecules in the same volume of nitrogen gas at the same temperature and pressure. If the density of argon is 1.425 times that of nitrogen, then an atom of argon is 1.425 times as heavy as a molecule of nitrogen. Since the nitrogen molecule contains two nitrogen atoms, an atom of argon is 2.85 times as heavy as an atom of nitrogen. The atomic weight of nitrogen is 14.0 and the atomic weight of argon must be 14.0 × 2.85, or just about 40.0.

This presented a problem immediately. If argon is added to the list of elements and is placed in the position one would expect of its atomic weight, then its valence breaks the neat rhythm exhibited by the other elements. You can see this in Table 4, where just the elements with atomic weights in the neighborhood of 40 are shown.

Table 4. Argon's Place in Order of Atomic Weight

Element	Approximate Atomic Weight	Valence
Sulfur	32.1	2
Chlorine	35.5	1
Potassium	39.1	1
Argon	40.0	0
Calcium	40.1	2

Rayleigh and Ramsay rightly felt that the rhythm of valence must not be upset. In two other places in the periodic table, as worked out by Mendeléev, a slightly heavier atom was pushed ahead of a slightly lighter atom in order to make the valence rhythm come out right. Very well, then, here one had to have another situation of this sort.

Strict adherence to the order of atomic weight gave the valences in the order 2, 1, 1, 0, 2. What was wanted was 2, 1, 0, 1, 2. All one had to do was to move argon ahead one place and put it in front of potassium. That portion of the list of elements would then become as shown in Table 5. The atomic weight

Table 5. Argon's Place in Order of Valence

Element	Approximate Atomic Weight	Valence
Sulfur	32.1	2
Chlorine	35.5	1
Argon	40.0	0
Potassium	39.1	1
Calcium	40.1	2

regularity was upset, but the valence rhythm was retained, and that was the more important.

Even so, there was considerable unrest in the chemical world about this. The existence of the new element, its inertness, and its monatomic state were disturbing enough in themselves. The fact that it could be squeezed into the periodic table only by violating atomic-weight order seemed to be a sure indication that something was wrong. Mendeléev himself balked and suspected that there was a mistake and that what Rayleigh and Ramsay called argon might really be triple-atom nitrogen (N_3) after all. This, after all, would have three times the weight of a nitrogen atom—or about 42. If one could only suppose N_3 to be inert, it would then answer the purpose as well as argon.

The New Column

If argon was to be accepted thoroughly, some sort of additional evidence would therefore have to be found that would nail down its shaky position in the periodic table. The evidence arose out of the fact that, if the periodic table were to have real value, argon could not exist as the only zero-valence gas. There had to be a whole family of such gases.

Mendeléev had arranged the periodic table in rows and columns in such fashion that elements with the same valence (and with very similar properties otherwise) fell into the same columns. Table 6 lists the columns in which the elements of

Table 6. Portion of the Periodic Table (as given in 1890)

Valence 2	Valence 1	Valence 1	Valence 2
	Hydrogen 1.0	Lithium 6.9	Beryllium 9.0
Oxygen 16.0	Fluorine 19.0	Sodium 23.0	Magnesium 24.3
Sulfur 32.1	Chlorine 35.5	Potassium 39.1	Calcium 40.1
Selenium 79.0	Bromine 79.9	Rubidium 85.5	Strontium 87.6
Tellurium 127.6	Iodine 126.9	Cesium 132.9	Barium 137.3

valence 1 and 2 belong, and includes under the name of each element its approximate atomic weight.

Notice, in Table 6, that iodine has a lower atomic weight than tellurium does. This is one of the cases in which Mendeléev altered the atomic-weight order. He did this so that he might place tellurium under the very similar selenium, and iodine under the very similar bromine—the similarity, in both cases, including not only valence but many other properties.

Suppose, now, that the Rayleigh-Ramsay suggestion is adopted and that argon is placed into the position between chlorine and potassium. The portion of the periodic table under discussion would appear as in Table 7.

But if argon exists between chlorine and potassium, then it must represent a whole family of such elements; and a new column is called for. There would have to be a noble gas between hydrogen and lithium, another between fluorine and sodium, and so on. We can number them thus:

Noble Gas 1: between hydrogen and lithium
Noble Gas 2: between fluorine and sodium
Noble Gas 3: between chlorine and potassium
Noble Gas 4: between bromine and rubidium
Noble Gas 5: between iodine and cesium

Argon itself is Noble Gas 3; now you can see why the search had to start for the other noble gases. If no other such gases could be found, then it would seem doubtful that argon could exist in its spot all by itself. In such a case, it would be evident that there was something wrong with the Rayleigh/Ramsay conclusions. If, however, the other noble gases were found and if their atomic weights permitted their insertions into the right places in the periodic table, then the Rayleigh/Ramsay conclusion with regard to argon would be triumphantly established.

Rayleigh, who was actually a physicist, felt the tug of his own science and no longer wished to linger in the alien realms of chemistry. It fell to Ramsay, therefore, to carry on.

Ramsay was alert for references in the literature to the appearance of any gas that had odd or suspicious properties, and was at once interested when he came across Hillebrand's report of four years earlier (see Page 15). Nitrogen, it seemed, was occluded by the uranium mineral uraninite, but the spectro-

Table 7. Portion of the Periodic Table (as given in 1894)

Valence 2	Valence 1	Valence 0	Valence 1	Valence 2
	Hydrogen 1.0		Lithium 6.9	Beryllium 9.0
Oxygen 16.0	Fluorine 19.0		Sodium 23.0	Magnesium 24.3
Sulfur 32.1	Chlorine 35.5	Argon 40.0	Potassium 39.1	Calcium 40.1
Selenium 79.0	Bromine 79.9		Rubidium 85.5	Strontium 87.6
Tellurium 127.6	Iodine 126.9		Cesium 132.9	Barium 137.3

scopic evidence raised a question. Unexplained lines were present.

Surely that was something to look into. There was no uraninite handy, but Ramsay was able to obtain some "cleveite," a very similar mineral.

He obtained the gas, just as Hillebrand did; when Ramsay studied its spectrum, he also found lines that were definitely not those of nitrogen. Furthermore, they were not the lines of argon, either.

Something about the unknown lines rang a bell. By March 1895, Ramsay had found the old report by Lockyer (see Page 14) and had convinced himself that the spectral line of the gas he had obtained from cleveite was the Janssen-Lockyer line found in the sun's spectrum. Ramsay turned to Crookes, the discoverer of thallium (see Page 13) and an expert in spectroscopic analysis. Crookes agreed with Ramsay's conclusion.

It became clear that Lockyer's "helium," the element of the sun, existed on earth after all. In honor of Lockyer, Ramsay kept the name, though he might, without argument, have adopted a new name to suit himself.* Hillebrand wrote to Ramsay, acknowledging his own misjudgment in not following up the puzzling lines. He generously gave Ramsay total credit for the discovery.

The properties of helium seemed to indicate that it, like argon, was a noble gas, for it did not react with other elements, and it was made up of single atoms. (All noble gases are monatomic, by the way.) To determine which noble gas it was, one needed only its atomic weight. From the density of helium, it was easy to see that the atomic weight was about 4.0. Consequently, it was clearly "Noble Gas 1," and belonged in the space between hydrogen and lithium.

---

* In a way, this is a pity. The ending "ium" ordinarily is reserved for metals, while "on," "en," and "ine" are reserved for the nonmetals. Helium is a nonmetal and should have been called "helion." All the other noble gases, like argon, have "on" endings.

Liquid Air

The discovery of helium was sufficient to establish argon in its position and to end all argument. Helium fit into place without any distortion of atomic weight. The possibility that this could be coincidence was too small to bother with. The new column existed!

Ramsay drove on all the harder in search of the remaining noble gases. In this, he was now joined by a young assistant, the English chemist Morris William Travers (b. 1872).

It seemed best to concentrate on the atmosphere. The noble gases were not expected to form compounds and therefore ought to exist in free, gaseous form. The proper place for free gases was the atmosphere. Argon had been found there; although helium was found occluded in minerals, it was also detected in the atmosphere a few months after Ramsay's announcement of its existence.

The search in the atmosphere was not going to be easy, however. Identifying argon had been a comparatively simple job because it made up about 1 per cent of the atmosphere; quite a large quantity, really. Helium was present in much smaller quantities, and the remaining noble gases might well be present in still smaller quantities. Poking through the myriads of molecules in the air to pluck out the occasional atom of the remaining noble gases could be most difficult.

Fortunately for Ramsay, the discovery of argon was no longer ahead of its time. A new development had just occurred that turned the nearly impossible into the quite possible. It came about this way.

For a hundred years, chemists had been trying to reach very low temperatures: temperatures at which all gases would become liquid. Some gases, such as chlorine or ammonia, were easy to liquefy. Chlorine became liquid at a temperature of $-34.6°$ C and ammonia at $-33.4°$ C. Chemists could attain such temperatures (not worse than a North Dakota winter day) with ease. They could even liquefy such gases at room temperature merely by putting them under sufficient pressure.

For a long time, however, such gases as oxygen, nitrogen, and hydrogen resisted their best efforts. Temperatures of − 100° C or lower were reached, and yet those elements remained gaseous. They even came to be called "permanent gases."

It was not until 1877 that a French physicist, Louis Paul Cailletet (1832–1913), managed to devise techniques that brought the temperature low enough to liquefy oxygen and nitrogen. It turned out that the former liquefied only at a temperature of − 183.0° C and the latter at the still lower temperature of − 195.8° C.

This meant that air itself, which was almost entirely oxygen and nitrogen, could be liquefied. For nearly twenty years after Cailletet's demonstration, the quantity that could be liquefied at any one time was very small and *liquid air* was available only for small-scale laboratory experiments.

In 1895, however, the very year in which Ramsay discovered helium, a German chemist, Karl von Linde (1842–1934), evolved methods for producing liquid air in quantity. This was fortunate, indeed, since liquid air could be checked for minor components much more easily than gaseous air.

If liquid is made up of a mixture of several components with different boiling points, these components can be separated by careful boiling, in a process known as *fractional distillation*. As the mixture boils, the component with the lowest boiling point comes off first. The first sample (or "fraction") of vapor is therefore particularly rich in that component. Later fractions are rich in a component of higher boiling point; still later samples are rich in components of still higher boiling points, and so on. The liquid that remains behind, shrinking in volume, gradually becomes richer in the components with the highest boiling points.

If liquid air is allowed to boil slowly, nitrogen, which has a lower boiling point than oxygen, comes off first. The early fractions of gas are nitrogen-rich, while the liquid air portions that remain behind are oxygen-rich. Indeed, the most convenient method for preparing pure nitrogen gas and oxygen gas since the early 1930's is by the fractional distillation of liquid air.

But what about any of the noble gases that might be present in the atmosphere? When air is liquefied, the noble-gas content is liquefied as well, and each individual noble gas might be isolated by very careful fractionation of the liquid air.

The boiling point of argon is − 185.7° C, which lies between those of oxygen and nitrogen. It tends to come off after nitrogen and before oxygen. There were good reasons for supposing that the noble gases denser than argon ("Noble Gas 4" and "Noble Gas 5") would have higher boiling points than oxygen; while the still-undiscovered noble gas that was less dense than argon ("Noble Gas 2") would have an even lower boiling point than nitrogen.

It followed, then, that if a quantity of liquid air were carefully distilled, the very first bit of gas that would come off would be rich in "Noble Gas 2." When almost all the liquid air had been slowly allowed to boil, the final bit of liquid left would be rich in "Noble Gas 4" and "Noble Gas 5."

Ramsay and Travers therefore turned to liquid air and obtained a liter of it in May 1898. They boiled it off carefully until only about 1/40 of the original quantity was left. They then allowed the final quantity to evaporate, trapping the gas, heating it, and studying it spectroscopically. It had a bright yellow line that was not quite in the position of any of the lines of helium, argon, or nitrogen.

Carefully, they measured the density of the gas and were able to show that it was considerably denser than argon. Indeed, from its density they were reasonably certain that it was "Noble Gas 4" and belonged between bromine and rubidium. It received the name *krypton,* from a Greek word meaning "hidden," because it had been hiding for so long, undetected, in the atmosphere.

The day after the discovery, young Travers was examined for his doctoral degree—and passed.

In searching for the remaining noble gases, Ramsay and Travers took a short cut. When oxygen and nitrogen were removed from the air by chemical reaction, leaving argon behind, all the other noble gases in the atmosphere were left behind, too, for the chemical reactions that sufficed to remove the oxygen and nitrogen touched none of the noble gases.

Instead of fractionating liquid air, therefore, why not fractionate liquid argon? Since argon made up only 1 per cent of the original air, the noble gases contained in the argon were a hundred times as concentrated there as they were in air. They should be that much easier to detect.

Immediately after the discovery of krypton, Ramsay and Travers liquefied 3 liters of argon to form not quite 4 cubic centimeters of liquid argon. This was carefully boiled, and the first fraction of gas at once yielded a spectrum that made it quite clear that "Noble Gas 2," between fluorine and sodium, had been located. It was named *neon*, from a Greek word for "new," as a result of a suggestion made by Ramsay's teen-age son. The discovery was made in June 1898.

Neon and krypton were present in the atmosphere in only tiny quantities. It seemed quite likely that the yet-undiscovered "Noble Gas 5" was present in still smaller quantities. Larger quantities of liquid argon would have to be used.

From these larger quantities, as much krypton was obtained as possible. This krypton was then liquefied and allowed to boil very slowly. "Noble Gas 5," if present, would be denser than krypton and would have a higher boiling point. Therefore, once most of the liquid krypton had been allowed to boil away, the last bit of liquid ought to be rich in "Noble Gas 5."

And so it was. The spectroscope gave it away at once, and

in July 1898, "Noble Gas 5," lying between iodine and cesium, was discovered. It was named *xenon,* from a Greek word meaning "stranger." (The "x" in xenon is pronounced like a "z.")

By July 1898, then, the portion of the periodic table we have been discussing looked like Table 8. Ramsay and Travers

Table 8. Portion of the Periodic Table (as given in July 1898)

Valence 2	Valence 1	Valence 0 (Noble Gases)	Valence 1	Valence 2
	Hydrogen 1.0	Helium 4.0	Lithium 6.9	Beryllium 9.0
Oxygen 16.0	Fluorine 19.0	Neon 20.2	Sodium 23.0	Magnesium 24.3
Sulfur 32.1	Chlorine 35.5	Argon 40.0	Potassium 39.1	Calcium 40.1
Selenium 79.0	Bromine 79.9	Krypton 83.8	Rubidium 85.5	Strontium 87.6
Tellurium 127.6	Iodine 126.9	Xenon 131.3	Cesium 132.9	Barium 137.3

had established a solid phalanx of noble gases, and all but argon fitted into place in terms of atomic weight as well as valence.

In 1904, Ramsay was awarded the Nobel Prize in chemistry for his discovery of the noble gases and for demonstrating their place in the periodic table. In that same year, Rayleigh also received the Nobel Prize in physics for his work on the density of nitrogen, which led to the discovery of the noble gases in the first place.

The discovery of the noble gases made it quite clear, by the way, that the composition of the atmosphere is complex indeed and that a number of trace components (with concentrations less than that of carbon dioxide) are present. The composition of the atmosphere, to the best of our present-day knowledge, is given in Table 9.

Table 9. *Composition of Air* (*as given now*)

Gas	Per Cent by Volume
Nitrogen (N_2)	78.084
Oxygen (O_2)	20.946
Argon* (Ar)	0.934
Carbon dioxide (CO_2)	0.033
Neon* (Ne)	0.001818
Helium* (He)	0.000524
Methane (CH_4)	0.0002
Krypton* (Kr)	0.000114
Hydrogen (H_2)	0.00005
Nitrous oxide (N_2O)	0.00005
Xenon* (Xe)	0.0000087

The values in Table 9 refer to the portion of the atmosphere near the earth's surface. Investigation of the atmosphere at great heights by means of rockets has shown that such unusual components as ozone, atomic nitrogen, atomic oxygen, and even sodium vapor are present in tiny quantities. At heights of hundreds of miles, the final thin wisps of atmosphere are made up largely of the lightest of all gases, helium and hydrogen.

Radioactivity

With three noble gases discovered in three successive months, there seemed reasonable grounds for supposing that Ramsay and Travers had uncovered the entire family of noble gases. All the obvious spaces allowed for by the periodic table were filled and no other noble gases were to be found in the atmosphere.

To be sure, there were signs that an additional row of elements might exist beyond those shown in Table 8. Thorium and uranium were two elements that might exist in that row, but, as

---

* Noble gas.

of early 1898, they were the only known elements that might exist there. That was not sufficient basis for a belief in the existence of a sixth noble gas.

However, while Ramsay and Travers were searching through liquid air, great things had been taking place elsewhere in the world of science.

In 1896, a French physicist, Antoine Henri Becquerel (1852–1908), had discovered (partly by accident, in a classic example of serendipity) that the heavy metal uranium was constantly giving out energetic radiations. In 1898, the Polish-French chemist Marie Sklodowska Curie (1867–1934) showed that this was true of the heavy metal thorium, too. Because these metals were actively giving off radiations, Madame Curie termed the phenomenon *radioactivity*. Uranium and thorium are examples of *radioactive elements*.

The atoms of radioactive elements, in giving off their radiations, change their nature and become other elements. This means that uranium and thorium are constantly breaking down (or undergoing *radioactive decay*) so that the quantity of those elements on earth is steadily decreasing. The rate of decrease is so slow, however, that the earth's supply of uranium will not be cut in half for 4.5 billion years. (This is the *half-life* of uranium.) The earth's supply of thorium, which breaks down even more slowly than uranium, will not be cut in half for fully 14 billion years.

As uranium and thorium undergo radioactive decay, other elements are formed that are, in their turn, radioactive; they break down much more rapidly than either uranium or thorium. These *daughter elements* are formed only slowly in the course of the long, drawn-out decay of uranium and thorium, and break down quickly. At any one moment, therefore, these daughter elements, caught between formation and breakdown, are present in the soil in only minute amounts.

Despite the ultratiny quantities present in the soil (even-in minerals rich in uranium and thorium) the daughter elements nevertheless make their presence known by the intense radiations they give off. Or, at least, they made their presence known once scientists were aware that such radiations existed, and learned to construct instruments for the detection of such radiation.

In 1898, Madame Curie became aware that some uranium minerals were far more radioactive than could be accounted for by their uranium content, and began to suspect the existence of these daughter elements (though she did not at the time realize that they arose from uranium and thorium breakdown). With the help of her husband, Pierre Curie (1859–1906), she treated several tons of uranium ore and isolated from it small quantities of two new elements.

The first of these was discovered in July 1898, the same month in which Ramsay and Travers had isolated xenon. The Curies named it *polonium* after Madame Curie's native Poland.

The second element, finally obtained toward the end of the year, was isolated as a compound with chlorine. This white salt glowed in the dark from the effect of the radiations (themselves invisible) on the glass of the containers holding it. The Curies named this element *radium*, therefore, in reference to the radiation.

The existence of polonium and radium extended the two columns of valence 2 in the periodic table, since polonium had to be placed under the very similar tellurium, and radium under the very similar barium.

Once polonium and radium were fixed in the periodic table, it was easy to see that elements must also exist in the valence 1 columns under iodine and cesium. These are formed in such small quantities and undergo radioactive breakdown so rapidly that they are present in the soil in unimaginably small traces; they were not actually discovered and named for forty years after polonium and radium had been located. Nevertheless, by 1898 chemists had sufficient faith in the periodic table to be certain that these other elements existed, whether they were discovered or not.

The discovery of polonium and radium also meant that another element must exist in the valence 0 column; a sixth noble gas directly underneath xenon. No ordinary methods sufficed to uncover "Noble Gas 6" in the atmosphere. Undoubtedly, it was radioactive and broke down so quickly that it simply did not accumulate in sufficiently large quantity to be detected.

In 1900, however, the German physicist, Friedrich Ernst Dorn (1848–1916), discovered that radium, in the course of its radioactive decay, gave off a gas. This gas, emanating from radium, was at first called *radium emanation*, straightforwardly enough. Radium emanation proved to be itself radioactive, and it was difficult to collect much of it. However, there was soon reason to think that it had the properties that were associated with noble gases, for it was quite inert. In 1910, Ramsay was able to lay his hands on a large enough supply to run a density determination and show that its atomic weight was such as to make it, without doubt, "Noble Gas 6." To make its name part of the family system (except for helium), "radium emanation" was changed to *radon*.

(Thorium, in the process of its breakdown, also yielded a radioactive gas, and so did a variety of uranium called "actino-uranium." These gases were first called *thorium emanation* and *actinium emanation;* respectively, then, as their noble-gas nature was recognized, their names were changed to *thoron* and *actinon*. Since radon, thoron, and actinon all proved to be varieties of the same noble gas, the term "radon" is almost universally used to include all three. To avoid favoritism, however, the neutral term, *emanon*, is sometimes used for "Noble Gas 6.")

With radon, the sixth and last noble gas was detected, and the portion of the periodic table that I have depicted three times earlier in the book can be written out as shown in Table 10.

Table 10. Portion of the Periodic Table (as given in 1910)

Valence 2	Valence 1	Valence 0 (Noble Gases)	Valence 1	Valence 2
	Hydrogen 1.0	Helium 4.0	Lithium 6.9	Beryllium 9.0
Oxygen 16.0	Fluorine 19.0	Neon 20.2	Sodium 23.0	Magnesium 24.3
Sulfur 32.1	Chlorine 35.5	Argon 40.0	Potassium 39.1	Calcium 40.1
Selenium 79.0	Bromine 79.9	Krypton 83.8	Rubidium 85.5	Strontium 87.6
Tellurium 127.6	Iodine 126.9	Xenon 131.3	Cesium 132.9	Barium 137.3
Polonium 210	?	Radon 222	?	Radium 226

4

Noble-Gas Atoms

Atomic Number

It is only fair to point out that the elegance of the periodic table is somewhat spoiled by the few instances where elements must be placed out of the proper atomic-weight order. I have already pointed out that argon and potassium are in the wrong order with respect to atomic weights; so are tellerium and iodine. A third case (the only other one) is that of cobalt and nickel, which are not shown in the portion of the periodic table that concerns us. Nickel comes after cobalt, although the atomic weight of nickel (58.7) is just a bit less than that of cobalt (58.9). This lack of elegance is particularly important with respect to the noble gases since it introduced considerable uncertainty as to the nature of argon when that gas was first discovered (see Page 32).

Shortly after the discovery of radon, however, a line of investigation was carried through that just about nullified the significance of the atomic weights so far as the periodic table is concerned. This came about as follows:

By 1909, experiments conducted by the New Zealand-born British physicist Ernest Rutherford (1871–1937) had shown convincingly that the atom was not a solid, tiny sphere of matter. Instead, it was mostly empty space, within which were to be found *subatomic particles,* each much smaller than an atom. At the center of each atom was a tiny *atomic nucleus,* which possessed nearly all the weight of the atom. Rutherford was therefore said to have demonstrated the existence of the *nuclear atom.*

The atomic nucleus invariably carried a positive electric charge, and around it there circled a number of *electrons,* each of which carried a negative electric charge. The electric charge of each electron is set equal to −1; in the ordinary atom there are just as many electrons present as are required to balance the positive charge on the nucleus, leaving a net electric charge of 0 for the atom as a whole.

For instance, the nucleus of a hydrogen atom has a charge of + 1, and the atom possesses one electron with a charge of − 1. The nucleus of the carbon atom has a charge of + 6, and the atom possesses six electrons with a total charge of − 6. In the same way the sulfur atom, with a nucleus possessing a charge of + 16, has sixteen electrons, while a uranium atom, with a nucleus possessing a charge of + 92, has ninety-two electrons, and so on.

The details of the nuclear charge and of how the size of that charge varies from element to element was worked out in 1913 by the English physicist Henry Gwyn-Jeffreys Moseley (1887–1915). From his work it could be deduced that all the atoms of a particular element have a characteristic positive charge on their nuclei, and that the charge for any one element would be different from that for any other.

Naturally, it occurred to chemists to define the elements by the characteristic size of their nuclear charge. This was termed the *atomic number*. Hydrogen, with atomic nuclei bearing a charge of + 1, was said to have an atomic number of 1. In the same way the atomic number of carbon was 6, that of sulfur was 16, that of uranium was 92, and so on.

The usefulness of the atomic number was particularly evident in connection with the periodic table. As the atomic number went up, so did the atomic weight, but not absolutely regularly. Sometimes, as the atomic number went up by 1, the atomic weight jumped quite a bit, and sometimes hardly at all. Once in a while, atomic weight even went down while atomic number went up. The cases of this last sort involved precisely those elements that had to be reversed with respect to atomic weight in order to be properly placed in the periodic table.

If the elements in the periodic table were listed in the order of atomic number, rather than atomic weight, no such reversals were necessary. For instance, iodine with an atomic weight of 126.0 comes after tellurium with the higher atomic weight of 127.6. If one goes by atomic number, however, iodine with an atomic number of 53 would naturally (and without reversal) come after tellurium with an atomic number of only 52.

Again, the necessity for distorting the periodic table in order to put argon in the right place is no longer necessary when atomic numbers are considered. Argon with an atomic weight of 40.0 seems to be placed out of order when it comes ahead of potassium with its lighter atomic weight of 39.1, but this becomes natural when you consider that the atomic number of argon is 18 while that of potassium is 19.

It becomes apparent, then, that it is atomic number, not atomic weight, that is fundamental in designing the periodic table. Furthermore, atomic number is always expressed in exact integers, while atomic-weight values are often far removed from exact integers.

It was only the fortunate circumstance that atomic weight almost always increased with atomic number (with only three exceptions) that made it possible for Mendeléev to construct the table at a time when atomic numbers were unknown.

Let me once again, then, draw that portion of the periodic table that includes the noble gases (see Table 11). This time I

Table 11. Portion of the Periodic Table (as given now)

Valence 2	Valence 1	Valence 0 (Noble Gases)	Valence 1	Valence 2
	1-Hydrogen	2-Helium	3-Lithium	4-Beryllium
8-Oxygen	9-Fluorine	10-Neon	11-Sodium	12-Magnesium
16-Sulfur	17-Chlorine	18-Argon	19-Potassium	20-Calcium
34-Selenium	35-Bromine	36-Krypton	37-Rubidium	38-Strontium
52-Tellurium	53-Iodine	54-Xenon	55-Cesium	56-Barium
84-Polonium	85-Astatine	86-Radon	87-Francium	88-Radium

shall omit the atomic weight and substitute the atomic number, placing it immediately before the name of each element. In addition, I shall include the two elements at the bottom of the valence-1 columns: *francium*, which was discovered in 1939, and *astatine*, which was discovered in 1940.

Isotopes

But the puzzle of the atomic weight remains. Why does the atomic weight go up with atomic number, but not evenly? Why does the atomic weight even reverse itself in some cases so that the atomic number might go up while the atomic weight goes down?

The answer arose out of the study of radioactivity. Uranium and thorium, in breaking down, produced so many different daughter elements that there simply was not room for all of them in the periodic table if an attempt were made to assign a separate place to each daughter element.

It occurred to several scientists, among whom the English chemist Frederick Soddy (1877–1956) usually receives the lion's share of credit, that it might be possible for more than one element to occupy the same place in the periodic table. In 1910, Soddy pointed this out in some detail, suggesting that a particular element might come in a number of varieties, each with different radioactive properties. All these varieties of a particular element would nevertheless have identical chemical properties and all would fit into the same place in the periodic table. Such varieties of a particular element he eventually called *isotopes,* from Greek words meaning "same place." As a particularly good example, Soddy pointed to radon, thoron, and actinon, which were clearly three varieties of one element. They had the identical chemical properties of a noble gas but differed in some radioactive properties, such as half-life.

It might seem that radioactivity was such a special and peculiar property that the existence of different varieties among the radioactive atoms could be accepted. But surely among the respectable *stable elements* (those that were not radioactive) one could adhere to the time-honored chemical notion that all atoms of a particular element were the same; that stable atoms could not be separated into different isotopes.

This view proved to be quite wrong, as was quickly shown by the English physicist Joseph John Thomson (1856–1940) in his work on the noble gas neon, in 1912.

Thomson worked with atoms from which some of the electrons had been stripped by the energy of an electric discharge. What remained of the atom carried a net positive electric charge, for there were no longer quite enough electrons left to neutralize all the positive electric charge on the nucleus. Such a positively charged remnant of an atom is called a *positive ion*.

The chemical symbol* for neon is *Ne,* so if one electron is removed from an atom giving it a positive charge of $+1$, the symbol for the ion becomes Ne^+. If two electrons were removed, there would be two positive units of nuclear charge unbalanced and we could speak of Ne^{++}. The ordinary neon atom, with the entire nuclear charge exactly balanced by the electrons, is a *neutral atom,* and it can be symbolized as Ne^0, or simply Ne.

Since an ion is electrically charged, it behaves differently from a neutral atom. An ion, for instance, is attracted or repelled by other electric charges or by magnetic poles, whereas a neutral atom is unaffected by either. Thomson directed a beam of ions through a magnetic field. Responding to this field, the ions followed a curved path, and, eventually, struck a piece of photographic film. When the film was developed, a darkened streak would indicate where the ions had struck.

The amount of curvature of the path followed by the ions depended partly on the size of the electric charge on the ions and partly on the atomic weight of those ions. Thomson knew that all the ions carried the same electric charge and he presumed that all neon atoms were alike in atomic weight. (It had been assumed for over a century that all the atoms of a particular element were alike in atomic weight.)

Therefore, Thomson fully expected that all the neon ions would follow the same curved path and form a single streak on the photographic film. He did obtain such a streak, but close by it he found a second, much fainter streak. From the positions he calculated that the more prominent streak was produced by

---

* The chemical symbols for the other noble gases, excluding argon, are helium, *He;* krypton, *Kr;* xenon, *Xe;* and radon, *Rn.* Argon is a special case. Alone among the noble gases, it was given a symbol consisting of a single letter, *A.* This irregularity finally proved disturbing to chemists and in the early 1960's it was decided to make the chemical symbol of argon *Ar.*

J

ions with an atomic weight of about 20, while the weaker streak was produced by ions with an atomic weight of about 22.

The result was checked a number of times. After the careful weighing of alternate possibilities, Thomson was forced to conclude that there were actually two varieties of neon; one of atomic weight 20, the other of 22. These can be termed neon-20 and neon-22, or, in chemical symbols, Ne^{20} and Ne^{22}. From the relative prominence of the streaks it could be calculated that neon was made up of those two varieties in the proportion of about 90 per cent neon-20 to 10 per cent neon-22.

The average weight of the atoms in any sample consisting of a mixture of 90 per cent with a weight of 20 and 10 per cent with a weight of 22 is 20.2, and that, actually, is the atomic weight of neon. This atomic weight, then, is *not* the weight of each of the supposedly identical atoms of neon, but merely the average weight of a collection made up of two different kinds of neon. (Later, very small quantities of a third variety, neon-21, were located, but not enough to affect the average weight by any significant amount.)

Neon, therefore, consisted of isotopes of different atomic weights—the atomic weight of an individual isotope usually being referred to as its *mass number*. The various isotopes were all neon, for all neon atoms, whether neon-20, neon-21, or neon-22, carried a nuclear charge of $+ 10$ and it is that charge that makes an atom a neon atom.

Thomson's assistant, the English chemist Francis William Aston (1877–1945), improved the device used for sorting out ions of different atomic weight. Aston's device, first constructed in 1919, was known as the *mass spectrograph*, and through the 1920's ions of various elements were sorted out into isotopes.

Of the 81 stable elements, no less than 61 are made up of two or more stable isotopes. Included among these 61 are all five stable noble gases. The isotopes of these gases are presented in Tables 12 and 13.

Table 12. Stable Isotopes of Helium, Neon, and Argon

Noble Gas	Isotope	Symbol	Occurrence in Gas (Per Cent)
Helium	Helium-3	He^3	0.0001
(atomic wt. = 4.0)	Helium-4	He^4	99.9999
Neon	Neon-20	Ne^{20}	90.92
(atomic wt. = 20.2)	Neon-21	Ne^{21}	0.26
	Neon-22	Ne^{22}	8.82
Argon	Argon-36	Ar^{36}	0.34
(atomic wt. = 40.0)	Argon-38	Ar^{38}	0.06
	Argon-40	Ar^{40}	99.60

Table 13. Stable Isotopes of Krypton and Xenon

Noble Gas	Isotope	Symbol	Occurrence in Gas (Per Cent)
Krypton	Krypton-78	Kr^{78}	0.35
(atomic wt. = 83.8)	Krypton-80	Kr^{80}	2.27
	Krypton-82	Kr^{82}	11.56
	Krypton-83	Kr^{83}	11.55
	Krypton-84	Kr^{84}	56.90
	Krypton-86	Kr^{86}	17.37
Xenon	Xenon-124	Xe^{124}	0.09
(atomic wt. = 131.3)	Xenon-126	Xe^{126}	0.09
	Xenon-128	Xe^{128}	1.92
	Xenon-129	Xe^{129}	26.44
	Xenon-130	Xe^{130}	4.08
	Xenon-131	Xe^{131}	21.18
	Xenon-132	Xe^{132}	26.89
	Xenon-134	Xe^{134}	10.44
	Xenon-136	Xe^{136}	8.87

As you see, there are 23 stable noble-gas isotopes. Xenon with 9 stable isotopes almost holds a record in this respect. It is bettered only by tin, which has 10 stable isotopes.

During and since the 1930's, scientists have formed various radioactive isotopes (about 1,300 altogether) of all the different elements, including the noble gases. These radioactive isotopes do not occur on earth, for if any had been formed at any time in the past, their rate of breakdown is so rapid that they would no longer exist.

If we consider the noble gases only, some typical half-lives are as follows: xenon-127, 36 days; krypton-87, 78 minutes; argon-37, 34.1 days; neon-24, 3.38 minutes; and helium-6, 0.82 second.

The longest-lived of all the known radioactive isotopes of the noble gases are argon-39, with a half-life of about 260 years, and krypton-81, with a half-life of about 210,000 years. A half-life of 210,000 years is long indeed, and if a sizable quantity of krpton-81 were formed we could count on its remaining in existence a long, long time. Its decline in quantity over the life span of a single individual would be insignificant. Nevertheless, even a half-life of 210,000 years is insufficient to keep an isotope in being over the vast multibillion-year lifetime of the planet earth. If any krypton-81 had been formed in ages past, it would be gone now.

One way in which even a short-lived radioactive isotope can remain in existence (at least in small traces) is to be continually produced through the breakdown of a more complicated, but long-lived, atom.

Thus, uranium consists of two isotopes, uranium-238 and uranium-235, each of which is long-lived. In the course of their slow radioactive breakdown, each is continually producing a different isotope of radon. Thorium consists of a single, long-lived isotope, thorium-232, and that, too, as it breaks down, produces an isotope of radon, differing from the two produced from uranium.

Radon therefore occurs in nature even though it possesses no stable isotopes. The naturally occurring radon isotopes are listed in Table 14. Other radioactive isotopes of radon can be

Table 14. Naturally Occurring Isotopes of Radon

Isotope	Symbol	Alternate Names	Half-Life
Radon-219	Rn^{219}	Actinium emanation; actinon	3.92 seconds
Radon-220	Rn^{220}	Thorium emanation; thoron	52 seconds
Radon-222	Rn^{222}	Radium emanation; radon	3.825 days

formed in the laboratory but do not exist in nature in measurable amounts. Of all the isotopes of radon, radon-222 (the original radium emanation) possesses much the longest half-life (short though it is). It therefore makes up virtually all the tiny traces of this element that are to be found on earth.

Protons and Neutrons

Knowing of the existence of isotopes and that the atomic weight represents an average, we can now see why argon seemed to be out of place in the periodic table as far as atomic weights are concerned.

Let us consider argon and potassium (the two culprits) in detail. The atomic number of argon is 18 and that of potassium is 19, so that argon comes ahead of potassium as is required if both are to be in the proper valence column.

Argon occurs in nature as a mixture of three isotopes with mass numbers of 36, 38, and 40; potassium occurs in nature as a mixture of three isotopes with mass numbers of 39, 40, and 41.

Although the mass numbers of the two sets of isotopes overlap, argon, with a lower atomic number, has two isotopes with a smaller mass number than any of the potassium isotopes. Potassium, with a higher atomic number, has one isotope with a higher mass number than any of the argon isotopes.

It is the distribution of the isotopes that is odd. In the case of argon, the light isotopes, argon-36 and argon-38, occur in the gas to only a small extent, and argon-40 makes up 99.60 per cent of all the argon atoms. Thus, the heaviest of the argon isotopes contributes preponderantly to the atomic weight, which comes out about 40.0.

In the case of potassium, it is the heavy isotopes that are rare, and the lightest isotope, potassium-39, makes up 93.08 per cent of all the potassium atoms, so that the atomic weight comes out 39.1. In brief, argon is most heavily weighted on its heavy end, so to speak, and potassium at its light end. The atomic weight of argon is therefore higher than one would expect from its list of isotopes and the atomic weight of potassium is lower. This same sort of situation also explains the atomic weight reversal in the case of the pairs cobalt-nickel and tellurium-iodine.

But now, another question arises. If there is an isotope, argon-40, and another isotope, potassium-40, in what way are they different? If both have the same mass number, how does it come about that they differ in atomic number?

The answer to that question was not worked out in its present form until the 1930's. It is now known that the atomic nucleus is itself built up of tiny particles called *nucleons*. These come in two varieties: *protons* (first given their name by Rutherford in 1920), and *neutrons*, discovered in 1932 by the English physicist James Chadwick (b. 1891).

The proton and neutron are very much alike. Both, for instance, possess a mass number of just about 1. The chief difference is that the proton carries a unit positive charge, $+1$, while the neutron carries no electric charge at all.

The positive charge on an atomic nucleus must be equal, therefore, to the number of protons it contains. If a nucleus contains 2 protons, its charge is $+2$. Conversely, if its charge is $+15$, we know it must contain 15 protons.

Since all the atoms of a given element have the same atomic number, and since this atomic number represents the size of the positive charge on the atomic nuclei, it follows that all the atoms of a given element have the same number of protons in their nuclei. Argon has an atomic number of 18 and therefore every argon atom, of whatever isotope, contains 18 protons in its nucleus.

The mass number of a particular atomic nucleus depends not only on the number of protons it contains, but on the number of neutrons as well, for the neutrons (even though they are uncharged and do not contribute to the atomic number) are as heavy as the protons and contribute just as much to the mass number.

Consider argon-36, for instance. The nucleus of an atom of argon-36 must contain 18 protons since the atomic number is 18. It must, however, also contain 18 neutrons; hence, the total mass number is 18 protons plus 18 neutrons, or 36. The mass number of an atom is equal to the total number of nucleons in its nucleus. By the same line of reasoning, then, argon-38 must have nuclei consisting of 18 protons and 20 neutrons; while argon-40 must have nuclei consisting of 18 protons and 22 neutrons.

The same principle holds for all other elements. The atomic number of potassium is 19; consequently, all potassium atoms must have 19 protons in their nuclei. Potassium-40 must be made up of 19 protons and 21 neutrons.

To summarize: Both argon-40 and potassium-40 contain 40 nucleons in their nuclei; but in the case of argon, the division is 18 protons and 22 neutrons, and in the case of potassium, 19 protons and 21 neutrons.

In Tables 15 and 16, the various naturally occurring noble-gas isotopes are listed, together with the proton-neutron make-up of their nuclei.

Once scientists came to understand the structure of the atomic nucleus, Prout's hypothesis (see Page 17) appeared in a new light. Hydrogen consists of two isotopes: hydrogen-1, which is very common, and hydrogen-2, which is quite rare. The atomic number of hydrogen is 1, so that both isotopes must have atomic nuclei containing but one proton. Since hydrogen-1 has a mass number of 1, the nuclei of atoms of hydrogen-1 must contain nothing but that one proton; no neutrons at all. We can therefore consider the proton as a hydrogen-1 nucleus.

The isotopes of the various elements have nuclei that are entirely made up of protons and of the very similar neutrons. In a way, then, the various isotopes are constructed of hydrogen nuclei, and Prout's suggestion that all the elements are made up of hydrogen was on the right track, at least.

Each isotope, therefore, has a mass number that is, indeed, a multiple of that of hydrogen, and that can, therefore, be expressed as an integer.* That the atomic weights of the elements themselves are often integers or nearly integers (a finding that guided Prout to his hypothesis in the first place) holds because many elements consist of atoms of a single isotope—as is true of fluorine, for instance, all of whose atoms are fluorine-19—or consist of a number of isotopes with one of them especially preponderant, as in the case of helium and argon (see Table 12). That some elements have atomic weights that are not integers does not mean that Prout's hypothesis is wrong after all, but that those elements are made up of a more or less even mixture of two or more different isotopes.

---

* The mass numbers are not, actually, *exact* integers. The small deviations from exactness are highly important in atomic physics, but need not concern us in this book.

Table 15. Nuclear Structure of Isotopes of Helium, Neon, and Argon

Isotope	Number of Protons (Atomic Number)	Number of Neutrons	Number of Nucleons (Mass Number)
Helium-3	2	1	3
Helium-4	2	2	4
Neon-20	10	10	20
Neon-21	10	11	21
Neon-22	10	12	22
Argon-36	18	18	36
Argon-38	18	20	38
Argon-40	18	22	40

Table 16. Nuclear Structure of Isotopes of Krypton, Xenon, and Radon

Isotope	Number of Protons (Atomic Number)	Number of Neutrons	Number of Nucleons (Mass Number)
Krypton-78	36	42	78
Krypton-80	36	44	80
Krypton-82	36	46	82
Krypton-83	36	47	83
Krypton-84	36	48	84
Krypton-86	36	50	86
Xenon-124	54	70	124
Xenon-126	54	72	126
Xenon-128	54	74	128
Xenon-129	54	75	129
Xenon-130	54	76	130
Xenon-131	54	77	131
Xenon-132	54	78	132
Xenon-134	54	80	134
Xenon-136	54	82	136
Radon-219	86	133	219
Radon-220	86	134	220
Radon-222	86	136	222

Rayleigh's careful work in determining the atomic weight of oxygen and hydrogen (see Page 19) was wasted as far as his primary purposes of checking Prout's hypothesis were concerned. Since it led serendipitously to the discovery of the noble gases, however, it remains one of the landmarks of nineteenth-century chemistry, and deservedly earned Rayleigh a Nobel Prize.

Electron Shells

Outside the nucleus are the electrons that make up the remainder of the atom. The number of electrons present in a particular atom is determined by the number of protons in the nucleus. To form a neutral atom the number of electrons outside the nucleus (each with a charge of -1) must be exactly equal to the number of protons inside the nucleus (each with a charge of $+1$). Therefore, the number of electrons present in a neutral atom must be equal to the atomic number of that element.

Since argon, for instance, has an atomic number of 18, each neutral argon atom must contain 18 electrons. This is true for any of the argon isotopes, for each different isotope possesses 18 protons in the nucleus. The isotopes vary only in the number of neutrons in the nucleus; since the neutrons carry no electric charge, they do not have to be neutralized, and therefore do not influence the electron content of the atom in any way.

The chemical properties of an atom depend on the number of electrons it contains. Since the atoms of all isotopes of argon possess the same number of electrons, they all possess the same chemical properties. It is this identity of chemical properties that allow us to include all the isotopes of argon as members of a single element.

Potassium, with an atomic number of 19, must possess 19 electrons in each neutral atom of each of its isotopes. All the isotopes of potassium have chemical properties different from all the isotopes of argon, because of this difference in electron content. Thus, potassium and argon are two different elements.

Again, although potassium-40 and argon-40 have identical mass numbers, the atoms of the former possess 19 electrons and those of the latter only 18, which gives them widely different chemical properties, and makes them members of different elements despite the identity of mass number.

Electrons are not merely distributed through the atom in higgledy-piggledy fashion. They are, instead, arranged in such a fashion as to seem to be distributed through a number of *electron shells* of increasing size from the nucleus outward.

The innermost electron shell, just outside the nucleus, can never hold more than 2 electrons; the next one can hold as many as 8; the next as many as 18; the next as many as 32, and so on. The most complex atoms we know, with slightly over 100 electrons per atom, have these electrons distributed through no fewer than seven electron shells.

Argon's 18 electrons, for instance, are distributed among three shells; 2 electrons are in the innermost shell, 8 in the next, and 8 in the one outside that. We can write this as 2/8/8.

To show the importance of this electron distribution, we can indicate the distribution of the electrons in the case of all the elements in that portion of the periodic table that contains the noble gases. We shall begin, in Table 17, with the two columns of the valence-2 elements, indicating the atomic number before the name of each element and the electron distribution under the name.

As you see, there are certain regularities in these electron distributions. The outermost occupied shell in the elements in the column headed by oxygen contains 6 electrons in every case. The outermost shell of the elements in the column headed by beryllium contains 2 electrons.

When two atoms collide, it is the electrons in the outermost shell that bear the brunt of the collision, so to speak. A chemical reaction involves a transfer of electrons from one atom to another (either in whole or in part) and the nature of this transfer depends almost entirely on the number of electrons in the exposed outermost shell.

Consider an atom of sulfur and one of selenium. The total number of electrons in the former is 16 and in the latter 34, so that the two atoms are members of different elements. However, the electronic arrangement in sulfur is 2/8/6 and in selenium is 2/8/18/6. Though the total number of electrons is different, the number in the exposed outermost shell is the same. Therefore, the chemical behavior of sulfur and selenium is quite similar, and although the two are different elements they were early recognized to be members of the same family of elements.

Oxygen, sulfur, selenium, tellurium, and polonium belong to what is usually called the *oxygen family,* after its first member. In the same way, beryllium, magnesium, calcium, strontium, barium, and radium belong to a family of elements usually referred to as the *alkaline earth metals* (for chemical reasons we need not go into).

In general, it is the experience of chemists that the arrangement of electrons is most stable when the outermost electron

Table 17. Electron Distribution in the Valence-2 Elements

Valence 2	Valence 2
	4-Beryllium 2/2
8-Oxygen 2/6	12-Magnesium 2/8/2
16-Sulfur 2/8/6	20-Calcium 2/8/8/2
34-Selenium 2/8/18/6	38-Strontium 2/8/18/8/2
52-Tellurium 2/8/18/18/6	56-Barium 2/8/18/18/8/2
84-Polonium 2/8/18/32/18/6	88-Radium 2/8/18/32/18/8/2

shell contains just 8 electrons. (The only exception is when the innermost shell is the only one present. It can hold 2 electrons at most, and a content of 2 is a very stable situation.)

Consider the magnesium atom with an electron arrangement of 2/8/2. If it were to give up the 2 electrons in the outermost shell, the arrangement of the remaining electrons would be 2/8, a particularly stable situation. In actual fact, then, the magnesium atom has a strong tendency to give up just 2 electrons. One electron can be transferred to each of two different atoms, so that the magnesium atom can end up forming a combination with two other atoms. It is for this reason that we say that magnesium has a valence of 2. For the same reason, all the other alkaline earth metals have a valence of 2.

Consider next the oxygen atom. Its electron arrangement is 2/6, but if it could gain 2 electrons, the arrangement would become the very stable 2/8. The oxygen atom, indeed, has a strong tendency to accept 2 electrons. It can accept one electron from each of two different atoms and end up forming a combination with two other atoms. It is for this reason that we say that oxygen has a valence of 2, and so do all the other elements of the oxygen family.

Indeed, the whole concept of valence (figured out in the 1850's from purely chemical data) depends on the electron distribution within the atoms. Since the periodic table was determined from considerations of valence, it, too, depends on the electron distribution within the atoms (although, to be sure, the details of electron distribution were not understood until fully half a century after the periodic table had been completed).

In Table 18, we next consider the two columns of valence-1 elements, which present a completely analogous situation.

Fluorine, chlorine, bromine, iodine, and astatine, each with 7 electrons in the outermost shell of their atoms, form a very similar group of elements, the *halogens*. Lithium, sodium, potas-

Table 18. Electron Distribution in the Valence-1 Elements

Valence 1	Valence 1
1-Hydrogen 1	3-Lithium 2/1
9-Fluorine 2/7	11-Sodium 2/8/1
17-Chlorine 2/8/7	19-Potassium 2/8/8/1
35-Bromine 2/8/18/7	37-Rubidium 2/8/18/8/1
53-Iodine 2/8/18/18/7	55-Cesium 2/8/18/18/8/1
85-Astatine 2/8/18/32/18/7	87-Francium 2/8/18/32/18/8/1

sium, rubidium, cesium, and francium, each with a single electron in the outermost shell, form another family, the *alkali metals*.

Each of the alkali metals can give up the single electron in the outermost shell and be left with 8 electrons in what becomes the outermost shell thereafter. Potassium, for instance, changes from 2/8/8/1 to the stable 2/8/8. Each of the halogens has a strong tendency to pick up one electron, so that chlorine will then change its electron distribution from 2/8/7 to 2/8/8. Both families therefore have a valence of 1.

(Hydrogen, with a single electron, can easily lose that electron or, somewhat less commonly, pick up an electron to form a stable number 2 for the innermost shell. For that reason, hydrogen is a rather unique element and is not truly a member of any well-defined family. It shares some of its chemical properties with the alkali metals and some with the halogens, but has distinct and important points of difference in each case.)

Now we are ready to consider Table 19, which deals with the electron distribution in the noble gases. As you see, each has an outermost shell containing 8 electrons (except for helium, which

Table 19. Electron Distribution in the Noble Gases

Valence
0

2-Helium
2
10-Neon
2/8
18-Argon
2/8/8
36-Krypton
2/8/18/8
54-Xenon
2/8/18/18/8
86-Radon
2/8/18/32/18/8

has 2 electrons in its single shell—an equivalent situation); therefore, it is not surprising that they form a definite family of elements. Furthermore, with 8 electrons in the outermost shell (or
2 for helium) there is no tendency either to give up electrons or
accept electrons in order to achieve a stable situation. The stable
situation is already present.

When I say that the noble gases do not tend either to give
up or take on electrons, I am saying that the noble gases do not
tend to react with other substances.* It is because of their stable-
electron distribution that the atoms of the noble gases are so
inert, standoffish, and "noble"; refusing to mix with other atoms
and form compounds; refusing even to combine among themselves, but remaining in gaseous form as single, separated atoms.

---

* They do not "tend" to react but, as we shall see, there are conditions
under which some of them do, nevertheless.

5

Noble-Gas Supply

The Constitution of the Universe

Earlier I said that the noble gases are sometimes called the "rare gases." Obviously, this is because they are rather rare on earth. Actually, however, some of them are anything but rare in the universe as a whole.

Astronomers, by studying the spectra of various stars and nebulae, as well as the absorption of light by the thin wisps of matter spread out between the stars, have made certain rough conclusions as to the relative abundance of the elements in the universe.

To begin with, the simplest element of all, hydrogen (atomic number 1), seems to be by far the most common substance in the universe. It is estimated that 90 per cent of all the atoms in the universe are hydrogen atoms. Another 9 per cent of the atoms are helium atoms (atomic number 2), the second simplest element. The remaining elements, all put together, make up less than 1 per cent of the atoms in the universe.

The distribution of elements in the universe is often presented on the basis of setting the arbitrary number of 10,000 for silicon atoms. The number of atoms of other elements are then given in proportion. Table 20 lists the abundance of the eleven

Table 20. Elemental Abundances in the Universe

Element	Number of Atoms in the Universe (Silicon = 10,000)
Hydrogen	400,000,000
Helium*	31,000,000
Oxygen	215,000
Neon*	86,000
Nitrogen	66,000
Carbon	35,000
Silicon	10,000
Magnesium	9,100
Iron	6,000
Sulfur	3,750
Argon*	1,500
Krypton*	0.51
Xenon*	0.040
Radon*	Negligible

most common elements in the universe, plus the rare noble gases. The table is based on an estimate prepared by the American chemist Harold Clayton Urey (b. 1893) in 1956. As you see, helium, neon, and argon are among the eleven most common elements. Only krypton, xenon, and, of course, radon can be considered the really rare "rare gases" on a universal scale.

This situation, in which matter generally is made up almost entirely of hydrogen and helium, is true of our own sun and is probably true of the giant planets on the outskirts of our own

* Noble gases.

system (Jupiter, Saturn, Uranus, and Neptune) if we can judge from spectroscopic data and from certain theories of how the sun's structure must be built up and how the solar system originated. It is also undoubtedly true for the vast majority of other stars and giant planets in the universe.

It is most certainly not true, however, of the earth. For every 10,000 silicon atoms in the universe, there are 400,000,000 hydrogen atoms; but for every 10,000 silicon atoms in the earth's crust, there are only about 1,320 hydrogen atoms. It is probable that the relative number of hydrogen atoms is lower still in the deeper layers of the earth's structure. However, the fine chemical details of the composition of those deeper layers are not known at all well, and there is no use discussing them.

Taking only the earth's outer layers into consideration, then, and assuming that no silicon was lost during the formation of the earth, we can conclude that we have only about 1/300,000 as many hydrogen atoms on our planet as might be expected from the composition of the universe.

The reason for this is not difficult to see. Solids and liquids are held firmly to the body of the earth through chemical attractions among the atoms and molecules, as well as by gravity. Gases are held by gravity alone. Individual atoms or molecules of gases are in rapid movement, and some of them work their way into the upper reaches of the atmosphere where the air is so thin that they will rarely collide with other atoms or molecules. Every once in a while one of these atoms or molecules in the upper atmosphere will build up a velocity greater than 7 miles per second. This is the *escape velocity* from earth. Anything (whether an atom or a rocket ship) moving more quickly than this, in a generally upward direction, can leave the earth and never return. For this reason, the atmosphere "leaks" and is constantly losing gas.

The greater the gravitational pull of a planet the higher the escape velocity, and the more rarely atoms or molecules manage to build up a velocity sufficiently high for the purpose. It is for this reason that Mars with ony 2/5 the gravitational pull of the earth has an atmosphere that is only 1 per cent as dense as the earth's. The moon, with a gravitational pull only 1/6 that of the earth, has managed to retain virtually no atmosphere at all. On the other hand, Jupiter, with a gravitational pull 2.6 times that of the earth (even at the top of its atmosphere, and undoubtedly a considerably stronger pull at its true surface), has a much thicker and deeper atmosphere than we have.

The lighter a particular atom or molecule, the more rapidly it tends to move, and the more likely it is to exceed escape velocity and leave the earth. Oxygen and nitrogen, for instance, consist of diatomic molecules with molecular weight of 32 (2×16) and 28 (2×14) respectively. Molecules this heavy can be retained by the earth. The leakage of these gases is imperceptible; if all goes as it has in the past, the earth can keep its atmosphere unchanged for many billions of years.

On the other hand, hydrogen, with diatomic molecules, has a molecular weight of only 2 (2×1). These molecules move much more rapidly than do those of oxygen and nitrogen; rapidly enough to surpass escape velocity quite often. For this reason, the earth cannot retain hydrogen gas, and only traces of hydrogen are found in the atmosphere. (Jupiter's stronger gravitational pull can retain hydrogen; hence, its atmosphere is rich in that gas.)

If hydrogen existed only in the form of hydrogen gas, then the earth would now be virtually without hydrogen. This is especially true since during its formation the earth was probably hotter (even considerably hotter) than it is now; the hotter the earth, the more rapidly all the gaseous atoms and molecules move. If hydrogen escapes from our atmosphere now, it would have escaped even more readily during the earth's infancy. Indeed, hydrogen would not have been captured by the forming earth in the first place.

However, hydrogen forms compounds, particularly water—

the molecules of which are built up of two hydrogen atoms and one oxygen atom (H_2O). Water vapor itself cannot be retained by a hot earth, but water molecules can, in turn, be bound more or less firmly to various mineral substances as *water of hydration*. Earth in its infancy may have lost (or never gained in the first place) all its gaseous hydrogen and all its water vapor, but it retained the water built into the chemical structure of its minerals. Later in its history, this water would be gradually forced out of combination to form the oceans (which, some geologists believe, are still in the slow process of formation).

In the same way, much gaseous oxygen and nitrogen (perhaps even all) was lost in the earth's infancy, but much was retained in the form of solid compounds.

Helium Formation

The situation with regard to the lighter noble gases, particularly helium, is like that of hydrogen, only more so. For every 10,000 atoms of silicon in the universe some 31,000,000 are helium, but for every 10,000 atoms of silicon in the earth's crust, only perhaps 0.004 are helium. The amount of helium on earth is only about a forty-billionth as much as one might expect from its amount in the universe as a whole.

Helium gas consists of single atoms with an atomic weight of 4. This is twice the molecular weight of hydrogen but is still too light for the earth's gravity to retain, particularly under the high-temperature conditions of the earth's infancy.

Furthermore, helium forms no compounds and exists only in the form of the elementary gas. Therefore, there is no device whereby some of the helium might be retained.

The wonder is, in fact, not that there is so little helium on earth, but that there is any helium at all. Why has it not all disappeared over the multibillion-year lifetime of the earth? Why is even a single atom left?

As it happens, it is quite likely that not a single atom of the original supply of helium (if any) is left. However, new supplies of helium atoms have been forming in the earth's crust through all its history.

This comes about because several long-lived radioactive elements give off *alpha particles* as they break down. In 1909, Rutherford was able to show that alpha particles were really helium nuclei. These picked up electrons very soon after they were ejected by the radioactive elements and became neutral helium atoms.

About 94.5 per cent of all the alpha particles formed in the earth's crust arises from atoms of uranium-238, each of which, as it breaks down, in stages, to atoms of lead-206, gives off no less than eight alpha particles. The rest are formed, almost entirely, from atoms of thorium-232, each of which breaks down, in stages, to lead-208, giving off six alpha particles. The rate of breakdown of these two substances is such that about 9,000 alpha particles are produced each second in each kilogram of the earth's crust.

This is not much, really, taken by itself; but there are a great many kilograms of matter in the earth's crust and there are a great many seconds in the year. A recent estimate based on the helium dissolved in the ocean depths suggests that, altogether, 120,000,000 cubic meters of helium are produced on earth, through radioactivity, each year—2,200 tons is what that volume amounts to.

Much of this helium remains trapped in the uranium and thorium minerals in which it is formed. Treatment of these minerals will liberate the helium, as Ramsay discovered and as Hillebrand failed to discover.

Some of the helium seeps out and mixes with other gases trapped within the earth's crust, particularly with the so-called "natural gas," actually a mixture of flammable hydrocarbons (possessing molecules, that is, made up of carbon and hydrogen). Natural gas is usually associated with petroleum, and sometimes when the natural gas in petroleum country is tapped, helium accompanies it.

The first discovery of this fact came about by accident. In 1903, a gas well was tapped near a Kansas town; to celebrate the occasion, a portion of the gas was drawn off to light a torch. The gas, however, refused to light. The astonished townsmen had it analyzed. Most of the gas was nitrogen, as it turned out, but nearly 2 per cent was helium.

The best helium sources are to be found among the natural gas wells in Texas. In particular, there are gas wells near Amarillo, which produce up to 13,600,000 cubic meters (250 tons) of helium each year. One well in Arizona produces a gas mixture that is 8 per cent helium. By the 1960's, the United States was producing over 2 billion cubic feet of helium per year.

Some of the helium formed in the earth's crust leaks into the atmosphere, of course. This occurs at a rate of, according to one recent estimate, two and a half liters per square mile per year. It cannot be retained in the atmosphere indefinitely, but some is always present—helium that has seeped upward from the ground and has not yet had time to leak out of the atmosphere into space.

The helium produced by the radioactive breakdown of uranium and thorium is entirely helium-4. How to account, then, for the small traces of helium-3 also present? Helium-3 is lighter than helium-4 and is even more readily lost from the atmosphere; therefore, if it is present at all, it must be continually formed.

And so it is. The earth is bombarded at all times and from all directions in space with very energetic *cosmic-ray particles.* They smash into the atmosphere, knocking atoms to pieces. Every once in a while, a nucleus of hydrogen-3 is formed. Such hydrogen-3, also called *tritium,* is the only known radioactive isotope of hydrogen. It breaks down, with a half-life of 12¼ years, and, in the process, turns to the stable helium-3 (sometimes called *tralphium*). This is the source of the traces of helium-3 found in the atmosphere; virtually none is present in the crust.

Argon Formation

Helium is relatively common for a "rare" noble gas, but it is not alone in this quality. Argon is surprisingly common, too. In particular, it makes up just about 1 per cent of the atmosphere, which is most astonishing for a noble gas. One might suspect that this is because its higher atomic weight makes it sluggish and therefore capable of being held by earth's gravity.

This is true nowadays; any argon now present in the atmosphere will be retained indefinitely. However, it is very likely that in the hotter times of earth's period of formation, any argon it may have possessed was lost, barring some tiny quantity physically trapped in minerals. The argon now present in the atmosphere must therefore have been formed in the eons since earth's early days.

One indication is the particular abundance of argon-40 which makes up 99.6 per cent of all the argon atoms on earth. In the universe as a whole, spectroscopic evidence seems to indicate that it is argon-36 that is the most common isotope. Apparently, then, it is the argon-40 in particular that must have formed since the planet settled down to cooler temperatures, after most of the argon-36 had been lost. Indeed, one recent suggestion is that such argon-36 and argon-38 as is present in the atmosphere is there because it was blown in from outer space by the solar wind; i.e., the particles forcibly blown out of the sun. Why then is argon-40 so common?

The blame, here, lies at the door of potassium. In 1906, a very weak radioactivity was found to be associated with potassium by the British scientist Norman Robert Campbell (the first time such a thing had been detected outside uranium, thorium, and their daughter elements). The radioactivity was quickly pinned down to potassium-40, the least common of the three naturally occurring potassium isotopes. Only about one potassium atom in 10,000 is potassium-40.

Potassium-40 breaks down with a half-life of 1,300,000,000 years. This is long enough to allow some of earth's original supply of potassium-4 to exist even today. It is short enough, however, so that over the total lifetime of the earth (at least five billion years) most of the original supply has vanished. Five billion years ago, there was at least 16 times as much potassium-40 as there is now, and about one potassium atom out of every 600 must have been potassium-40.

Still, potassium is one of the most common elements in the earth's crust. Even though potassium-40 nowadays makes up so little of the potassium supply, there is still about as much potassium-40 in the earth's crust as there is uranium. Furthermore, the potassium-40 is very widely spread so that its radioactivity cannot be lightly dismissed.

Potassium-40 was recognized, almost at once, as an example of radioactive breakdown by way of *beta-particle* emission. (A beta particle is a speeding electron.) An atom that emits a beta particle increases its atomic number by one.

In 1936, however, the Japanese physicist, Hideki Yukawa (b. 1907) showed that it was possible for some atoms to undergo radioactive breakdown by absorbing an electron from the innermost electron shell. The innermost electron shell is called the K-shell, so that the process is called *K-capture*. K-capture, involving the absorption of an electron, produces an effect in an atom that is opposite that produced by beta-particle emission, which involves the output of an electron. In K-capture, the atom decreases its atomic number by one.

By 1938, the American physicist Luis W. Alvarez (b. 1911) had shown the reality of K-capture. Potassium-40 broke down by K-capture, for instance, as well as by beta-particle emission. Fully 89 per cent of the potassium-40 atoms that broke down gave off beta particles. The atomic number increased from 19 to 20, and such atoms became calcium-40. The remaining 11 per cent, however, underwent K-capture, the atomic number decreased from 19 to 18, and the atoms became argon-40.

It is the K-capture process undergone by potassium-40 that, over the eons, has produced the large quantity of argon-40 in the atmosphere, and that accounts for the preponderance of argon-40 over argon-36 and argon-38.

There remains considerable argon in the soil, of course. Even though it leaks out slowly into the atmosphere, this doesn't happen immediately; there is probably 2,500 times as much argon in the soil as there is in the atmosphere.

In fact, by comparing the potassium content of particular rocks with the argon-40 content, one can work out the length of time since the rock has become solid and, therefore, in a condition to trap any argon-40 that is formed. A known quantity of potassium can produce argon-40 at a known rate, and from the quantity of argon-40 present one can then determine how long it has been collecting.

Naturally, one must be sure that no argon-40 has leaked out of the rock during the time it has collected. There is always the chance that it has done so and the chance, therefore, that the age figure obtained is too small. Even so, some rocks have been found that have registered an age of 2,500,000,000 years by this method. The ages of meteorites have also been tested in this way; some meteorites have been found to be as old as 4,500,000,000 years.

You might suppose that the same system can be applied to uranium and thorium minerals by determining how much helium has been collected over the ages as a result of the radioactive breakdown of those heavy metals. Unfortunately, helium, having a much smaller atomic weight than argon, leaks out of rocks considerably more rapidly. Chemists therefore determine age by measuring the quantity of lead produced by uranium and thorium breakdown. It was such determinations in the first couple of decades of the twentieth century that added the final proof to the suspicion that the earth was actually several billion years old.

Noble Gases in the Atmosphere

All the noble gases occur in nature only as the elementary gas. Helium and argon, which are continually being formed in the soil, leak into the atmosphere—where one would expect to find any gas. As for neon, krypton, and xenon, which are not formed in the soil to any significant extent, they are found only in the atmosphere.

The relative proportions of the various noble gases in dry, filtered atmosphere can be presented as the number of atoms of each present for every million molecules of oxygen and nitrogen. We do this—listing the noble gases in order of increasing atomic weight—in Table 21.

Table 21. Atom Abundances of the Noble Gases in the Atmosphere

Noble Gas	Atomic Weight	Number of Atoms per Million Molecules of Nitrogen and Oxygen
Helium	4.0	5.25
Neon	20.2	18
Argon	40.0	9,300
Krypton	83.8	1
Xenon	131.3	0.08
Radon	222	0.00000000000006

Neon has an atomic weight of 10, but this is entirely too light for the earth's gravity to hold at the elevated temperatures of the planet's infancy. Nor have any new supplies formed in the soil. It is a combination of these two reasons that makes neon on earth so much rarer than argon. There are about 60 times as many atoms of neon as of argon in the universe as a whole, but on earth there are over 1,000,000 times as many argon atoms (counting the supply in the soil) as there are neon atoms.

The neon present in the atmosphere now is probably built up out of small traces that were mechanically trapped in rocks at the beginning and have since been released into the air as the rocks underwent weathering. That which is now present in the air will probably be held over a long period. Indeed, earth's ability to hold neon, where it cannot hold the lighter helium, is shown by the fact that there are three times as many neon atoms in the atmosphere as there are helium atoms, even though helium is constantly seeping upward from the soil and neon is not.

Krypton and xenon can be held easily by the earth's gravity, perhaps even under the hotter conditions of the planet's early days. Their rareness in the atmosphere reflects the fact that krypton and xenon are actually rare, even in the universe as a whole.

A small amount of krypton and xenon arises in the earth's soil through the breakdown of uranium—but not through the ordinary radioactive breakdown. Every once in a while, a uranium atom breaks into two nearly equal portions, a process called *uranium fission.*

This process can be hastened under the proper circumstances and tremendous energies are then released (forming the first *atomic bombs*). Even without encouragement, however, occasional *spontaneous fission* takes place. The event is very rare and uranium-238, for instance, undergoes spontaneous fission with a half-life of about 6 quadrillion years. This means that for every 1,300,000 uranium-238 atoms that undergo ordinary breakdown, a single uranium-238 atom undergoes spontaneous fission. Even so, in the earth's crust taken as a whole, some 10 grams of uranium must be undergoing fission every second.

The uranium atom does not undergo fission in precisely the same fashion each time. A whole group of *fission products* is formed, and among them are several isotopes of krypton and xenon.

The amount of krypton and xenon so formed, even over the lifetime of the earth, is not great, but the existence of the process is of possible importance in connection with the moon.

The moon has so small a gravity that it is unable to retain any molecules (or free atoms) less massive than argon. Even argon can probably be retained only temporarily. Krypton and xenon, however, have atoms massive enough to remain even in the moon's gravitational field.

This fact does not make it possible for the moon to have an atmosphere in our sense, but there are faint wisps of gas near its surface, enough to make an "atmosphere" at least a ten-trillionth the density of ours. Such an "atmosphere" would be nothing but a very good vacuum on earth, but it is much denser (rare though it is) than the incredibly thin wisps of gas in interplanetary space. It is quite probable that much of this lunar atmosphere is made up of krypton and xenon obtained from uranium fission in the moon's crust, and that some argon may also be present, at least temporarily, as it forms from potassium-40.

That leaves only radon to mention. It is sluggish enough to be held in place by the earth's gravitational field without trouble. However, it breaks down very quickly after it is formed and the tiny traces in the atmosphere represent the few atoms just produced from uranium breakdown that have not yet had time to break down in their turn.

Although the noble gases are among the least common of the stable elements, it is a lot easier to separate substances out of the air than out of the soil. Consequently, the noble gases are more easily available than if they made up a part of some equivalently rare mineral.

Furthermore, the total supply of the noble gases in the atmosphere is respectable. We must realize, to begin with, that the atmosphere represents a sizable mass of material. Its weight is no less than 57,000,000,000,000,000 tons (57 million billion tons). Gases that make up even small portions of such a large mass can be isolated in considerable quantity.

From the abundance of the atoms of the various noble gases, and allowing for the different weights of the atoms, the total supply of the stable noble gases in the atmosphere is shown in Table 22.

Table 22. Total Mass of the Stable Noble Gases in the Atmosphere

Noble Gas	Total Atmospheric Supply (Tons)
Helium	40,000,000,000
Neon	710,000,000,000
Argon	400,000,000,000,000
Krypton	20,000,000,000
Xenon	1,000,000,000

In addition, there are about 1,000,000,000,000,000 (1 million billion tons) of helium in the soil and perhaps 1,000,000,000,-000,000,000 (1 billion billion tons) of argon. The potential supply of the noble gases, rare though they may be, lies in the billions of tons. Even xenon, which is probably the rarest of all the stable elements, exists in a one billion ton supply.

It is interesting to see how this supply can be divided among the various isotopes of the noble gases. In particular, how much is there of the rarest stable isotope of each of the five stable noble gases? These rarest isotopes are helium-3, neon-21, argon-38, krypton-78, and xenon-126. The atmospheric supply* of each is given in Table 23. Helium-3 is the rarest stable isotope on earth; even so, it is present in the atmosphere in the tens of thousands of tons.

Table 23. *Total Mass of Some Stable Noble-Gas Isotopes in the Atmosphere*

Noble-Gas Isotope	Total Atmospheric Supply (Tons)
Helium-3	40,000
Neon-21	1,850,000,000
Argon-38	240,000,000,000
Krypton-78	70,000,000
Xenon-126	900,000

The truly rare noble gas is, of course, radon, since it is radioactive. The total supply of radon in the atmosphere is a little over 500 tons (though there may be considerably more than this trapped among the uranium minerals of the earth's crust.

---

* The helium and argon in the soil are almost entirely in the form of helium-4 and argon-40. The atmospheric supplies of helium-3 and argon-38 are virtually all there are of those isotopes, therefore.

6

Uses of Noble Gases

Argon

Since argon is the most common of the inert gases and forms such a respectable portion of the atmosphere, it is easy to produce it in quantity by the fractional distillation of liquid air. It is also comparatively cheap; a dollar will buy about 300 liters of argon these days. Argon first came into large-scale use in connection with electric light bulbs.

Electrical lighting became practicable in 1879, when the American inventor Thomas Alva Edison (1847-1931) heated a carbon filament in an evacuated glass bulb by means of an electric current. The carbon glowed to a white heat, but did not melt, for the melting point of carbon is something like 3,500° C, well above the temperature of even a glowing filament in a light bulb.

Although incandescent carbon filaments do not melt, they

are quite brittle when white-hot, and break easily. In 1904, metal was deposited on the carbon filament to make it stronger. In 1906, carbon was abandoned altogether in favor of high-melting metals, and tantalum (melting point 2,850° C) came into use. In 1911, methods were devised for drawing tungsten (melting point 3,390° C) into thin wires and that metal replaced tantalum and is still in regular use in incandescent bulbs today.

Although the metal wires proved much stronger than the carbon filaments, they still broke prematurely in the vacuum. There is, apparently, a slow evaporation of hot metal within the light bulb. Atom by atom, the metal lifts free of the wire and settles down on the inner surface of the glass bulb. Not only does this reduce the transparency of the glass and dim the light, but it causes the filament to grow thinner, more brittle, and, eventually, to break.

The vacuum seemed necessary, for if the filaments were heated in the presence of air, they would combine with oxygen in a flash and be destroyed. The American chemist Irving Langmuir (1881–1957) realized that in order to prevent this it was sufficient to remove merely the oxygen and not the air as a whole. He therefore filled light bulbs with nitrogen.

Since nitrogen is an inert gas, it does not react readily with metal filaments. By the pressure of its presence, however, it cuts down the rate at which the metal evaporates. Light bulbs lasted much longer when nitrogen-filled than when evacuated.

In 1914, Langmuir took the next logical step. Nitrogen is inert but not completely so, and it does react with the metal slowly. In the place of nitrogen, therefore, he substituted argon, which was a little more expensive but which increased the lifetime of the bulbs more than enough to compensate for the additional cost. Electric light bulbs are routinely argon-filled now, so that the first important industrial use of the noble gases still retains its value.

The inertness of argon is its most important single characteristic as far as uses are concerned. This is true in light bulbs, and it is true so far as argon's connection with welding is concerned.

When metals are welded, a junction where two separate pieces of metal meet is partially melted and then allowed to solidify into a single piece of metal. During World War I, it became customary to make use of *arc-welding,* in which an electric spark is made to jump from an electrode to the material being welded. The joint is heated like the filament in a light bulb and melted.

The great difficulty of arc-welding was that the metal (usually steel) reacted with the oxygen and even the nitrogen of the air during the moments when it was white-hot. The joint was therefore riddled with oxides and nitrides (combinations of the metal with oxygen and with nitrogen). These oxides and nitrides are brittle and can fatally weaken the joints. As a result, metallurgists strove to devise methods for protecting the areas to be welded, and keeping air away.

In 1929, a useful solution was found. A jet of argon gas was pushed through the arc so that it constantly enveloped the area to be welded. Such *shielded arc-welding* produced excellent joints of full strength, not only in steel, but in other metals such as copper, nickel, magnesium, and so on. The most important single use of argon is in connection with shielded arc-welding nowadays. (Nor is argon wasted in the process; it is merely returned to the atmosphere from which it was originally taken so that the gas remains in essentially limitless supply.)

Argon is also used on other occasions where it is important to keep oxygen and nitrogen away. For instance, aluminum can be cut by an "atomic hydrogen torch." In such a torch, hydrogen molecules are broken up into separate atoms, and these atoms are allowed to reunite in the neighborhood of the aluminum being cut. The reunion produces so much heat that the aluminum is cut through almost at once. However, in the presence of air, the melting aluminum combines readily with oxygen, and the brittle oxide flakes away, so that the cut is ragged and irregular. For that reason, argon is added to the hydrogen. It doesn't affect the reunion of hydrogen atoms, but does serve to surround the melting aluminum with an inert atmosphere.

Argon is also used in the preparation of metallic titanium. Titanium is a common metal that was scarcely ever used prior to World War II because it was thought to be so uselessly brittle. But the brittleness was not the fault of the metal but of the oxides and nitrides that were always produced whenever titanium was prepared in metallic form in the presence of air. Today titanium is prepared under an atmosphere of argon, and the resultant pure titanium is particularly tough and strong. It is stronger than steel, weight for weight, and is therefore achieving many important uses.

Other elements, like silicon and germanium, must be prepared as extremely pure crystals in order to have them serve adequately as components of new types of electrical equipment called *transistors*. The necessary purity can be achieved when the crystals are grown under argon.

Neon

Since the other noble gases are also inert, they would be used in place of argon were it not that no other noble gas is as cheap as argon. Neon, for instance, is nearly five hundred times as expensive as argon. However, neon and the other noble gases have their more restricted uses.

When an electric current is forced through a tube containing a quantity of gas or vapor at low pressure, the temperature of the gas or vapor is raised to the point where it gives off light of the particular color of its spectral lines. The result is a *vapor lamp*.

The first one to come into use was the mercury vapor lamp,

invented in 1901. It gives off a bright light, tinged with bluish-green, which was very useful in factories in the days when ordinary electric light bulbs were still rather dim. However, there are virtually no red lines in the mercury spectrum, signifying that there is nothing for red objects to reflect. Lips are black in the light of the mercury vapor lamp, complexions mottled, and the generally unpleasant appearance of the human face and skin makes the mercury vapor lamp unusable in the home.

The sodium vapor lamp produces a bright yellow light, which makes it unusable in the home, too. The yellow light, however, is particularly visible under conditions of fog and mist; consequently, such lamps sometimes are used to light up highways.

It was early discovered that the noble gases glowed beautifully when used in vapor lamps. Neon, in particular, yielded a bright red glow. When Ramsay and Travers were preparing to study its spectrum, its distinctive glow told them at once that a new element was present.

The French chemist Georges Claude (1870–1960) worked with neon vapor lamps; beginning in 1927, he was able to produce them in quantity. Vapor lamps containing a variety of different gases or gas mixtures could be bent into attractive shapes, or into letters that spelled out words (and usually carried an advertising message). So prominent was the red color of those vapor lamps containing neon that all of them, whether they actually contained neon or not, came to be called *neon lights*.

A small, dim version of the neon light is the *neon glow lamp*, which consists of a small bulb containing electrodes in a neon atmosphere. Electricity is forced through the neon, causing it to produce a red glow. Little electricity is required for the purpose, and the lamp is really not intended for illumination, but merely as a signal—to indicate the location of a switch or to act as evidence that some electric circuit is in working order (or, perhaps, is not in working order).

Neon lights were not suitable for home use, either. For

everyday illumination, white light was needed, and the necessary
vapor lamp was not produced until the 1940's. When it came, it
was by way of the mercury vapor lamp.

A mercury vapor lamp releases a certain amount of ultraviolet light. Since ultraviolet light does not pass through ordinary
glass, the vapor lamp is safe to use. (If quartz is used, the ultraviolet light will pass through, and a "sun lamp" is produced
with which people can achieve a tan and take advantage of any
therapeutic use of ultraviolet light; but then, of course, they must
guard against sunburn and eye-damage.)

If the inner surface of the mercury vapor lamp is coated
with a fluorescent substance, it will blaze with white light when
exposed to ultraviolet. The white light will penetrate the glass
and we have *fluorescent lights*. Fluorescent lights are whiter
than ordinary incandescent bulbs, are brighter for a given con-
sumption of electric power, are cooler, and are longer-lasting.
Since World War II, fluorescent lights have been steadily re-
placing the ordinary light bulb.

Fluorescent lights require a "starter": something that will
act to heat the electrodes and start the electric current flowing
through the vapor. A common starter is an argon glow lamp.

Neon is used in several dramatic devices that have come into
use only recently.

In 1957, the *spark chamber* was introduced for the detection
of subatomic particles, and proved to be more efficient for many
purposes than the older detection devices. The spark chamber
consists of closely spaced metal plates, with alternate plates
highly charged with electricity, so that an electric spark is at
the point of being released. When a subatomic particle speeds
through, sparks are released at the points where it strikes the
plates. Between the plates of this device an inert gas is used,
usually either neon or argon.

More exciting still is the *laser*. This device produces a beam
of intensely energetic light, the rays of which can be kept tightly

bound and which have but a single wavelength. No light of this sort had ever been produced by man or (so far as we know) by nature before 1960, when the American physicist Theodore Harold Maiman (b. 1927) produced the first laser.

This first laser had, as its key constituent, a crystal of synthetic ruby. The crystal was first charged with energy, which it was then made to release as a very brief flash of intense red light. The first laser was, therefore, intermittent.

Efforts were made at once to produce continuous lasers, and the ruby was replaced by tubes of gas. The *gas lasers* so produced, later in 1960, were continuous. The gases used in such lasers include all the stable noble gases, alone or in combination. The first gas laser, produced by the Iranian physicist Ali Javan (b. 1926), working at Bell Telephone Laboratories, made use of a mixture of neon and helium. This variety is still the most important.

Krypton and Xenon

Fluorescent lamps may contain mixtures of argon and krypton. Krypton can also be used in ordinary light bulbs. Indeed, krypton is superior to argon for the purpose, for the denser the gas, the greater the slowing effect upon the rate of evaporation of the metallic filament.

Since krypton is produced from air in only relatively small quantities and is about nine thousand times as expensive as argon, it is unlikely that krypton will replace argon on a large scale. Still, krypton can be used for special lamps which will then last much longer than argon-filled lamps of equivalent brightness (or will be much brighter than argon-filled lamps of equivalent life expectancy).

Krypton possesses a useful radioactive isotope of intermediate half-life. Long-lived radioactive isotopes such as argon-39 (half-life, about 260 years) and krypton-81 (half-life, about

210,000 years) are too feebly radioactive to be very useful. Short-lived ones such as argon-41 (half-life, 1.83 hours) and krypton-79 (half-life, 34.5 hours) fade out too quickly to be useful.

Krypton-85, however, avoids either extreme. It has a half-life of 10.6 years and is therefore sufficiently active and long-lived to be useful.

It can be used, for instance, to test for leaks in sealed containers. If even small quantities of krypton-85 get through the walls of such a container, they can be detected through the radiation it gives off; the presence of a leak is then known. Krypton-85 can be detected in far smaller concentration than nonradioactive gases can possibly be, so that krypton-85 is remarkably sensitive as a leak detector. Since it is inert, krypton-85 can be relied upon not to react, chemically, with anything in the container—which gives it an advantage over most other radioactive isotopes that might otherwise serve the purpose.

Krypton-85 can also be used in a fluorescent lamp that will remain luminous for years without a power supply. The radiation of the krypton-85 will keep the fluorescent powder glowing.

Xenon, also obtained from liquid air (but with greater difficulty than krypton, since xenon is less common), is about twice as expensive as krypton. It, too, can be used in special lights where the expense is justified.

In general, elements absorb X-rays with increasing efficiency as the atomic number increases. Xenon, with an atomic number of 54, consequently is quite efficient as an X-ray absorber. Since it is a gas, it can be pumped into various body cavities easily; since it is a noble gas, it reacts with nothing in the body and, in the quantities used, does no harm. No other element possesses so complex an atom while remaining a gas at ordinary temperatures, so that no other element can quite combine the convenience and absorptive powers as xenon does.

Among the noble gases, the greater the atomic number, the

more soluble the gas in water and in body fluids. In general, substances that dissolve in body fluids often display anesthetic effects. The noble gases do, and since xenon is the heaviest of the stable noble gases, it is the most soluble and the most efficient anesthetic.

A mixture of 20 per cent oxygen and 80 per cent xenon will produce deep anesthesia quickly. There is no danger of explosion or fire, as when ether is used; there are no unpleasant side-effects; and the patient wakes up quickly once the gas is no longer administered. The only thing that stands in the way of practicability is the expense.

Xenon, in vapor lamps, gives a bluish light, while krypton gives a greenish one.

Even rare radon has had its uses. After radium was discovered, its intense radioactivity came to be used as a device to kill cancer cells. Since the radiation could also convert normal cells into cancerous ones, the use of radium was not without its danger.

Small quantities of radon (produced by the radium) could be used for the purpose after it had been sealed within small glass tubes. The radon radiations die down much more quickly than do those of radium, for radon has a much shorter half-life (3.8 days as compared to 1,620 years for radium). The radon needles therefore could be used and, in a sense, forgotten.

Since World War II, however, a wide variety of radioactive isotopes of the various elements has come into production; these isotopes have replaced radon in cancer therapy.

7

Helium

Lightness

In the previous chapter only helium received no special attention. This is not because it is unimportant, but, on the contrary, because it is so unusually important that it deserves a chapter to itself.

For one thing, helium is an element of extremes. It is made up of the second simplest of all atoms and is therefore less dense than any element but hydrogen (which has the simplest of all atoms).

The density of two different gases under similar environmental conditions is in proportion to the weight of the particles making them up (provided the gases are not under too high a pressure or too low a temperature). Thus, hydrogen is made up of molecules, containing two hydrogen atoms each, and possessing, therefore, a molecular weight of 2. Helium is made up of single atoms with an atomic weight of 4. Since 4 is twice 2, the density of helium is twice that of hydrogen. At 0° C and ordinary atmospheric pressure, the density of hydrogen is 0.09 grams per liter; that of helium is 0.178 grams per liter.*

One way of treating these densities is to put them into everyday terms. Imagine a living room 18 feet long, 12 feet wide, and 7 feet high. Such a room filled with hydrogen at 0° C would contain 8.5 pounds of that gas. It would contain 17 pounds of helium, if that were used instead. These weights may seem astonishingly large considering how light gases seem to us, but the same living room contains 123 pounds of ordinary air.

If we arbitrarily set the density of air equal to 1, we can list the densities of a number of common gases (including all the noble gases) as shown in Table 24. As you see, there are only eight common gases (if we include water vapor as a gas) that are lighter than air, and only three common gases that are less than half as heavy as air.

Just as objects lighter than water can float on water, gases lighter than air (if prevented from mixing with air) will float in air.† This point was first put to practical use in 1783, when two French brothers, Joseph Michel Montgolfier (1740–1810) and Jacques Étienne Montgolfier (1745–1799), held a light bag, open end downward, over a flame and let it fill with hot air. Since hot air is less dense than cold air, the hot air rose, carrying the bag with it. This was the first *balloon*.

---

* Hydrogen gas made up of molecules consisting of pairs of hydrogen-2 atoms would have a molecular weight of 4, while a gas made up of helium-3 exclusively would have an atomic weight of 3. Thus, a kind of helium could be lighter than a kind of hydrogen. However, hydrogen-2 and helium-3 are quite rare. Ordinary hydrogen and helium are almost entirely hydrogen-1 and helium-4, respectively, and will be treated that way.

† An object lighter than water floats on the water's surface, because water has a surface to float on. A gas lighter than air rises, but finds a top level for air thins out and grows less dense with height, while the floating gas, penned in a container, can only expand so far. Eventually, it is no longer less dense than the air about it and then it no longer rises.

However, hot air is only slightly less dense than cold air; as soon as the hot air cools it is no longer less dense. Something better was needed if balloons were to be practicable. Hydrogen had been described by Cavendish only seventeen years earlier (see Page 8), and was the one gas then known to be definitely and considerably lighter than air. The French physicist Jacques Alexandre César Charles (1746–1823) suggested it be used to fill balloons. This advice was immediately followed, and ballooning became quite a fad in the years before and after 1800.

A century later, in 1900, the German inventor Count Ferdinand von Zeppelin (1838–1917) mounted an engine on a gondola suspended under a cigar-shaped balloon and thus achieved the first *dirigible balloon* (one that could be "directed").

Table 24. Densities of Various Gases

Gas	Density (Air = 1)
Hydrogen (H_2)	0.069
Helium* (He)	0.138
Neon* (Ne)	0.345
Methane (CH_4)	0.54
Ammonia (NH_3)	0.59
Water vapor (H_2O)	0.62
Carbon monoxide (CO)	0.97
Nitrogen (N_2)	0.97
Air ($O_2 + N_2$)	1.00
Oxygen (O_2)	1.10
Hydrogen sulfide (H_2S)	1.17
Hydrogen chloride (HCl)	1.26
Argon* (Ar)	1.38
Carbon dioxide (CO_2)	1.52
Chlorine (Cl_2)	2.45
Krypton* (Kr)	2.89
Xenon* (Xe)	4.53
Radon* (Rn)	7.65

* Noble gases.

Throughout all the nineteenth century and well into the twentieth, hydrogen was the gas used to inflate balloons and dirigibles even though it represented a terrible safety hazard because of its flammability and explosiveness. German dirigibles that attempted to bomb London during World War I were completely ineffective because they were such large, fat targets and were so ridiculously easy to set on fire.

Yet there seemed no substitute. The only other lighter-than-air gases of any consequence that were available in the nineteenth century were methane and ammonia. These were denser than hydrogen, of course, and had less lifting power. In addition, methane was almost as flammable as hydrogen, and ammonia was foul-smelling and toxic.

The discovery of the noble gases offered a way out. In the first place, two of them, neon and helium, were lighter than any other gases but hydrogen itself. Their lightness is more effective than would seem from density figures alone. The density of helium is twice that of hydrogen, and the density of neon is five times that of hydrogen. This does *not*, however, mean that their lifting power is one half and one fifth, respectively, of hydrogen.

Consider it this way. If a volume of gas displaces 1 pound of air, the air exerts an upward pressure of 1 pound upon the displacing gas. If we consider a volume of air weighing 1 pound, the same volumes of hydrogen, helium, and neon weigh 0.069, 0.138, and 0.345 pound, respectively (as is to be expected from the relative densities of those gases).

This means that 0.069 pound of hydrogen displaces 1 pound of air, and the air pushing upward with a pressure of 1 pound will lift the 0.069 pound of hydrogen plus 0.931 pound of anything that may be attached to it—since $1 - 0.069 = 0.931$. By the same reasoning, air will lift 0.138 pound of helium plus 0.862 pound attached to it; and will lift 0.345 pound of neon plus 0.655 pound attached to it.

In other words, if a given volume of hydrogen will lift 0.931 pound, the same volume of helium will lift 0.862 pound and that volume of neon will lift 0.655 pound. Helium has 0.862/0.931 or nearly 94 per cent the lifting power of hydrogen, despite the fact that helium is twice as dense as hydrogen. Similarly, neon has 70 per cent the lifting power of hydrogen, though it is five times as dense as hydrogen.

Helium and neon, particularly helium, are thus possible substitutes for hydrogen. The slight loss in lifting power involved in the use of helium is totally unimportant when you consider that helium is absolutely nonflammable, nonexplosive, nontoxic, odorless, tasteless—harmless in every way.* In addition, helium, with its heavier atoms, escapes through the fabric of the enclosing bag at a smaller rate than does hydrogen.

Since the only source of neon is the atmosphere, it is far too expensive for use in balloons. Helium, which is much to be preferred, is produced in such large supply from natural gas wells (see Page 73) that it is cheap enough to use for the inflation of balloons for children at carnivals. It is quite practicable to produce helium even in the quantities required to inflate giant balloons and dirigibles. (Helium-3, however, the rare helium isotope, costs about $100 per liter.)

During World War I, the United States was already bending its efforts toward the collection of sufficient helium for use in balloons; after World War I, helium was the gas used by the United States for that purpose, as well as by those nations able to purchase helium from the United States.

In the 1930's, Germany, which was the world's foremost builder of dirigibles, was unable to buy American helium, because its National Socialist regime was anathema to the vast

---

* Of course, if you breathe an atmosphere consisting entirely or nearly entirely of helium, you will die in minutes. It will not be the helium that will kill you, but merely the lack of oxygen. As long as you have an adequate supply of oxygen, you can breathe all the helium you wish.

majority of Americans. As a result, German dirigibles remained
hydrogen-filled. The largest and most elaborate of the German
dirigibles, the "Hindenburg," flew to its destination at Lake-
hurst, New Jersey, in early May of 1937. On May 6, as it tried to
land, its 6.7 million cubic feet of hydrogen burst into flames and
was destroyed with the loss of thirty-five lives. That was the end
of hydrogen-filled balloons and dirigibles.

Unfortunately, the helium-filled dirigibles built by the
United States and other nations also met their doom in the
1930's. They did not catch fire but their large and comparatively
flimsy structure could not withstand the stress of storms.

Nevertheless, there are many uses, even today, for small
blimps (advertising, for instance) and for large balloons intended to rise into the upper atmosphere for scientific purposes.
Such balloons, routinely inflated with helium, rise twenty miles
above the earth's surface and have an advantage over rockets in
that they can remain there for hours and even days.

Inertness

The fact that helium is completely inert, and relatively inex-
pensive, makes it as useful, potentially, as argon for such things
as shielded arc-welding and for use in the metallurgy of metals
sensitive to oxygen and nitrogen. However, helium has other
important uses for which argon cannot substitute. For that reason, wherever argon and helium can be used for some purpose
equally well, it makes sense to use argon.

Argon cannot substitute for helium, of course, whenever
extreme lightness is required. Argon cannot be used to inflate
balloons, for instance. The lightness of helium, which makes it
useful for balloons, makes it useful also in some aspects of
medical treatment.

Suppose an artificial atmosphere is made up of 21 per cent
oxygen and 79 per cent helium; an atmosphere, in other words,
in which helium replaces nitrogen and argon. A person breath-

ing such an atmosphere gets all the oxygen he needs, and is not deprived of anything he needs (if we assume the mixture to contain small amounts of water vapor and carbon dioxide) for he makes no use of nitrogen or argon, anyway.

Such an oxygen-helium atmosphere possesses only one third the over-all density of the ordinary oxygen-nitrogen atmosphere. It is less viscous and flows more easily through narrow passageways. Patients suffering from asthma, or from any other condition that constricts their nasal and bronchial passages, can inhale and exhale more easily and get the oxygen they need, where the ordinary atmosphere might doom them to slow strangulation. Hydrogen would be even better than helium were it not that an oxygen-hydrogen mixture is almost literally dynamite that explodes at a spark.

Helium can replace nitrogen under conditions where the presence of nitrogen is not merely a matter of indifference to the body, but where it becomes an agonizing danger.

Again we encounter the question of solubility. All gases will dissolve in body fluids to some extent, and we can judge the comparative extents to which they dissolve by considering the solubility of gases in water, which makes up the bulk of body fluids. Some gases are very soluble in water. One hundred cubic centimeters of cold water (about a fifth of a pint) will dissolve about 120,000 cubic centimeters of ammonia and about 50,000 cubic centimeters of hydrogen chloride. These are exceptional cases. Other gases are much less soluble than this.

Some of the common gases (but excluding the noble gases) are listed in order of decreasing solubility in Table 25.

Such small solubilities must not be shrugged off. The oceans of the world contain fifty times as much carbon dioxide as the atmosphere does and they form a vital reservoir of the gas. The sea animals that breathe by way of gills utilize the small quantity of oxygen dissolved in sea water.

Then, too, even though the body makes no use of gaseous nitrogen at all, some of it dissolves in the body fluids. The solubility of gases generally increases with pressure and this fact is important to those men who work under high pressure.

This applies particularly to workers in caissons under water, for instance. They must breathe an atmosphere that is maintained at a pressure equivalent to the water pressure about them if they are to build tunnels under rivers—pressures equal to two or three times that of the ordinary atmosphere. Under such circumstances, oxygen and nitrogen both dissolve to an unusual extent in the body fluids. The oxygen is consumed by the body but the nitrogen remains untouched in solution. If the pressure is then rapidly decreased, the nitrogen can no longer remain in solution but comes bubbling out in the joints and in the blood stream. It can produce agonizing pain and, under extreme conditions, can kill. This condition is called "caisson disease" or, more commonly, "the bends." Consequently, when workers leave their caissons, they must first remain in decompression chambers, in which the pressure is slowly reduced so that the nitrogen bubbles out in stages and at a rate no greater than can be handled by the body.

Now let us consider the solubilities of the noble gases, in order of decreasing atomic weight, as listed in Table 26. As you see, the solubility decreases as the atomic weight grows smaller. Xenon is five times as soluble as oxygen (its solubility was mentioned earlier in connection with the use of xenon in

Table 25. Solubilities of Some Common Gases

Gas	No. of Cubic Centimeters Dissolved in 100 Cm³ Cold Water
Carbon dioxide	170
Oxygen	4.89
Carbon monoxide	3.5
Nitrogen	2.33
Hydrogen	2.14

anesthesia). Xenon is used for that purpose only at ordinary pressure, however, so that when the patient is no longer breathing it, it does not bubble out of the tissues but can be disposed of little by little. Its use does not involve the danger of bends. Radon would be even more efficient as an anesthetic were it not for its radioactivity.

As for neon and helium, they are less soluble than either oxygen, nitrogen, or hydrogen. In fact, helium, because of its extreme inertness, is the least water-soluble gas known.

Therefore, when an oxygen-helium atmosphere is used in caissons, only about a third as much inert gas is dissolved in body fluids as when an ordinary atmosphere is used. The bubbles that emerge on decompression are smaller and fewer. In addition, since helium flows more easily than nitrogen, helium bubbles are more easily disposed of. The use of an oxygen-helium atmosphere makes possible more rapid decompression and decreases the danger of bends.

One minor difficulty involved in breathing helium arises from the fact that small atoms vibrate more rapidly. Sound waves are therefore higher-pitched, and men find themselves speaking in a squeaky soprano. Sometimes this upsets men so much that they must communicate by writing.

Table 26. Solubilities of the Noble Gases

Noble Gas	No. of Cubic Centimeters Dissolved in 100 Cm³ Cold Water
Radon	51
Xenon	24
Krypton	11.0
Argon	5.6
Neon	1.47
Helium	0.94

Liquefaction

It is in connection with low temperature, however, that helium is most unusual and most irreplaceable.

If the temperature is low enough to begin with, an element is in the *solid state*, in which the atoms (or molecules) making it up are held in a fixed position; they can vibrate, but they cannot break away altogether.

As the temperature is made to rise, the atoms or molecules vibrate more rapidly and energetically until they no longer remain in the neighborhood of any fixed position at all, but slip and slide freely about each other. The element has entered the *liquid state* and the temperature of transition is the *melting point*.

In a liquid, the atoms or molecules, though free to move about, must remain in virtual contact with one another. As the temperature continues to rise, however, atomic vibration increases until finally the atoms or molecules pull apart altogether and separate, moving with complete independence thereafter. The element has entered the *gaseous state* and the temperature of transition is the *boiling point*.

In the case of each element, there are attractive forces holding atoms or molecules together. The energy of vibration must overcome these forces if the solid is first to melt, and if the liquid that results is then to boil. Naturally, the more tightly the neighboring atoms or molecules are held together, the higher the melting point and boiling point must be.*

---

* This holds true for compounds, too. However, as the molecules of a compound gain energy, so do the individual atoms making up the molecule. The molecules can vibrate to pieces, so to speak, before the boiling point, or even the melting point, is reached. Such compounds are said to *decompose* on heating. Many compounds do, however, have clear melting and boiling points and decompose only at temperatures well above the boiling point. Diatomic elements can be made to decompose into individual atoms if heated to a high enough temperature but this, too, usually takes place well above the boiling point.

Carbon is an example of an element in which there are unusually tight interatomic attractions. The electrons of the carbon atom (atomic number 6) have the arrangement 2/4. To achieve stability, the carbon atom may gain part or all of four additional electrons in order to have the stable configuration 2/8 (see Page 64).

If a carbon atom is in close proximity to a second carbon atom, each can contribute an electron to a common pool; and, if the two carbon atoms remain in contact, both shared electrons can be counted in the outermost shell of each atom. Each has gained one of the four additional electrons it needs.

If a carbon atom does this with four other carbon atoms, forming a two-carbon pool with each, it will have gained four electrons altogether and will have the required eight electrons in its outermost shell. Each of the other carbon atoms must do the same and each of the carbon atoms they attach themselves to must also do the same, and so on—in a kind of "chain-letter" fashion. The result is that in any ordinary piece of carbon, uncounted numbers of carbon atoms are clinging together in order to possess the stable arrangement of eight electrons in the outermost shell. To pull those atoms apart means upsetting that stable arrangement; and to do this requires a very high temperature. At atmospheric pressure, carbon does not melt till a temperature of over 3,500° C is reached; its boiling point is 4,200° C.

A number of metals have electronic structures that make it possible for individual atoms to cling so tightly together as to possess high melting and boiling points. Tantalum melts at about 3,000° C and tungsten at 3,400° C. Both boil at temperatures of almost 6,000° C.

In other cases, atoms cling together less tightly and a lower temperature suffices to pull them apart. Mercury melts at −39° C, so that it is liquid at room temperature (and on pretty cold days, too)—the only metal of which this is true. Its boiling point is at 357° C.

Atoms may cling together tightly, but in doing so may form small molecules which themselves have very little mutual attraction. Thus, the oxygen atom (atomic number 8), with its electron arrangement of 2/6, requires only two electrons to reach the stable situation of 2/8. It forms a two-electron pool with each of two hydrogen atoms. When that is done, the oxygen atom has eight electrons in its outermost shell, and the hydrogen atoms each have two. (The hydrogen atoms, with but a single electron shell, require only two electrons for stability.)

This means that the atom combination H_2O must remain in being to retain that electron arrangement, and this comprises the molecule of water. The molecule of water need combine with no other atoms to achieve stability for the atoms of which it is composed, so that it is largely self-contained. There is only feeble attraction between one water molecule and the next; the melting point of water is 0° C and the boiling point is merely 100° C.

One oxygen atom can form a four-electron shared pool with another oxygen atom. It will then form a molecule, O_2, which is even more self-contained. Neighboring oxygen molecules exert so feeble an attraction for each other that a very low temperature, – 183° C, suffices to boil it.

In order to consider the boiling points of substances such as oxygen in better perspective, let us begin at the bottom. There are a number of theoretical reasons for supposing that there is a lowest possible temperature at – 273° C. This lowest possible temperature is called *absolute zero.*[*]

In 1848, William Thomson, later Lord Kelvin (1824–1907), suggested that one could use a temperature scale that would start at absolute zero and then go up by centigrade degrees. Such a scale would be an *absolute scale,* measuring *absolute*

---

[*] To be as exact as possible, the currently accepted value of absolute zero is – 273.16° C.

temperature. Such temperatures are now signified as A (for absolute) or K (for Kelvin).

The melting point of ice (0° C) is 273 degrees above the absolute zero, so the melting point of ice can be given as 273° K. Any centigrade temperature can be converted to an absolute temperature by adding 273 to the centigrade figure. Thus, the boiling point of water (100° C) is 100 + 273 or 373° K.

In dealing with the boiling point of gases such as oxygen, it is particularly useful to use absolute temperatures. If we say that oxygen boils at − 183° C, we know only that this is a very cold temperature. However, if we say instead that it boils at 90° K, we know that it boils at a temperature that is only 90 degrees higher than the absolute limit of cold.

As I remarked earlier in the book the chemists of the late nineteenth century were trying hard to attain temperatures low enough to convert all gases into liquids. By the 1890's oxygen, nitrogen, and carbon monoxide had been liquefied and liquid air had become a commercially available product. Only hydrogen remained unconquered. In 1898, however, the Scottish chemist James Dewar (1842–1923) succeeded in dropping the temperature to the point where hydrogen was liquefied.

In Table 27 are listed the boiling points of the most re-

Table 27. Boiling Points of Some Low-Boiling Gases

Gas	Boiling Point (° K)
Oxygen	90
Fluorine	85
Carbon monoxide	81
Nitrogen	77
Hydrogen	20

calcitrant of the gases (excluding the noble gases), those with boiling points at temperatures less than 100° K. It is no wonder that hydrogen held out for twenty years as the sole known unliquefied gas. Its boiling point is 57 degrees lower than that of nitrogen, only a little over a quarter as far from absolute zero as the boiling point of nitrogen.

But by 1898, the noble gases had been discovered. Even as hydrogen was liquefied, it proved no longer to be the champion as far as low boiling points were involved.

The noble gas atoms already possess eight electrons in the outermost shell (two in the case of helium's only shell) and need form no combinations to attain that mark. They are individually self-contained and there is an unusually low amount of attraction between their atoms. This attraction decreases as the atomic weight decreases; similarly, the boiling point becomes lower as the atomic weight decreases, as can be seen in Table 28.

Table 28. Boiling Points of the Noble Gases°

Noble Gas	Boiling Point (°K)
Radon	211.3
Xenon	165.1
Krypton	119.8
Argon	87.3
Neon	27.1
Helium	4.2

The boiling point of radon is fairly high, – 62° C. This means that on a record cold day in Antarctica, radon might just barely liquefy. Xenon and krypton boil at lower temperatures, but they are not unusual in this respect.

The three lightest noble gases, argon, neon, and helium, enter the exclusive circle of those gases with boiling points less than 100° K—a group that includes only eight members: seven elements (oxygen, argon, fluorine, nitrogen, neon, hydrogen, and helium) and one compound (carbon monoxide).

° Noble gases are listed in order of decreasing atomic weight.

The boiling point of argon is somewhat below that of oxygen, and the boiling point of neon is somewhat above that of hydrogen. Indeed, in cases where liquid hydrogen is needed in small quantities and where there is a danger of fire, liquid neon (considerably more expensive but quite inert) is an excellent substitute.

Helium has the boiling point that sets the record, however. It was not until 1908 that the Dutch physicist Heike Kamerlingh-Onnes (1853–1926) managed to liquefy helium. With that, the final victory was won over the gases. Kamerlingh-Onnes was awarded the Nobel Prize for physics in 1913 for this feat. Nowadays, helium is easily liquefied and some special refrigerating devices can produce more than 100 liters of liquid helium an hour. About 80,000 liters per year are produced in the United States, and its price is not much over $6 per liter.

Liquid helium introduced the scientist to a completely new world. Its boiling point is five times as close to absolute zero as that of hydrogen. As far as the retention of ultracold temperatures is concerned, nothing will substitute for helium, nothing at all. As long as liquid helium exists, nothing exposed to it can be at a temperature greater than 4.2° K. The new science that involves the study of phenomena at such low temperatures is called *cryogenics.**

Naturally, once ultracold temperatures had been achieved, it was possible not only to liquefy the low-boiling gases, but to solidify them as well. The melting points for the noble gases, plus those other gases with boiling points below 100° K, are given in Table 29.

---

* In a way, ordinary helium does not quite hold the record for boiling points. If helium-3 is separated and collected, it proves to have a boiling point of 3.2° K, fully a degree lower than that of helium-4. However, helium-3 is so rare a substance that its only value lies in helping theoretical physicists explain the structure of matter and its behavior at ultracold temperatures. It has no practical uses.

Table 29. Melting Points of Some Gases

Gas	Melting Point (° K)
Radon*	202
Xenon*	161
Krypton*	117
Argon*	84
Carbon monoxide	74
Nitrogen	64.3
Oxygen	54.8
Fluorine	50
Neon*	25.5
Hydrogen	14.0
Helium*	—

You can see that at the temperature of liquid helium (4.2° K and lower) there are not only no remaining gases, there are no remaining liquids. Even hydrogen is a solid.

As for helium itself, no melting-point figure is given in Table 29. The reason is that even at absolute zero there is still some energy left in a system. This *zero-point energy* cannot be removed; consequently, one cannot achieve anything colder than absolute zero, but that zero-point is there just the same. Although it is very small, it is sufficient to jostle the helium atoms out of any fixed position they may try to take up, so feeble is the attraction between helium atoms. For this reason, helium does not solidify at ordinary pressures, even at absolute zero. In a universe at absolute zero, all substances would be solid with the sole exception of helium, which would be liquid. Solid helium can exist, however, at pressures that are not ordinary. If a temperature less than 1.1° K is attained and, at the same time, a pressure equal to 25 times that of our atmosphere, then helium will solidify. Helium was first successfully solidified in 1926 in Kamerlingh-Onnes' laboratory just a few months after the death of Kamerlingh-Onnes himself.

---

* Noble gases.

The Neighborhood of Absolute Zero

In 1935, scientists in this same laboratory found that when liquid helium was cooled below 2.2° K, it underwent a remarkable alteration in properties. It was as though there were two completely different forms of helium. The form above 2.2° K is called *helium I* and behaves like an ordinary liquid (except, of course, for its extreme frigidity). The form below 2.2° K, *helium II*, behaves like no other liquid on earth. It behaves almost as though it were a gas rather than a liquid.

For one thing, the viscosity (ease of flow) of helium II is even less than that of a gas; only one thousandth as great as that of the least viscous gas, hydrogen. The less viscous a substance the more easily it flows through narrow openings; the result is that virtually nothing is leakproof as far as helium II is concerned. A seal may be gas-tight and yet not helium II-tight. This phenomenon is called *superfluidity*.

Again, helium II can conduct heat with phenomenal rapidity, about 800 times as rapidly as the next most heat-conductive substance, copper. As a result, it is impossible to maintain temperature differences, however slight, within a sample of helium II for any significant length of time. If one portion of a sample of helium II is heated, the added heat spreads to all other portions almost at once.

Since all of helium II is at the same temperature at the same time, there can be no boiling in the ordinary sense of the word. In an ordinary liquid, such as water or, for that matter, helium I, there can be local "hot spots," places where the temperature momentarily rises above the boiling point with the consequent formation of a bubble of gas. These bubbles form and agitate the liquid in a manner with which anyone who has watched water boil is familiar.

No such local hot spots can form in helium II; no such bubbling and agitation can take place. As helium II gains heat, layers of atoms peel off the top surface, and that is all. Helium II boils with absolute evenness and quiet.

Because helium II is so low in viscosity it has no difficulty in layering itself over any solid with which it comes in contact. In doing so, it forms a layer 50 to 100 atoms thick. If helium II is in a test tube, it forms a layer (quite invisible to the eye) over the inner surface all the way up to the mouth, then over the lip and down the outer surface (*film flow*). It then drips off the bottom of the test tube until the test tube is empty. To anyone observing the phenomenon for the first time, it would seem as though the test tube had a hole in the bottom.

On the other hand, if an empty test tube is sealed into a container and partially immersed in a quantity of helium II, the liquid will layer itself onto the outer surface of the test tube, up to and over the lip, and will drip into the test tube interior until the level is equal inside and outside the test tube.

Helium II transmits sound in a very unusual way. In addition to sound traveling as a wave of alternating increased and decreased pressure, it also travels as a wave of alternating increased and decreased temperature (*second sound*). This has been explained by presuming that helium II is actually a mixture of helium II and helium I (the mixture varying in proportions with different temperatures) which flow through each other in opposite directions.

Theoretical physicists are fascinated by the odd way in which helium II behaves; from its behavior they have tried to evolve certain fundamental conclusions as to the structure of matter. Oddly enough, helium-3 when cooled to very low temperatures shows no sign of undergoing the same change helium-4 does. Liquid helium-3 always seems to be in the helium-I form and to remain an ordinary liquid at all times.

Helium is not the only substance that gains unexpected and unusual properties at liquid-helium temperatures. In 1911, Kamerlingh-Onnes was measuring the electrical resistance of mercury at the temperature of liquid helium. He expected the resistance to reach unprecedentedly low values, for the resistance of metals to electric flow ordinarily drops as temperature decreases. He did not, however, expect the resistance to disappear altogether. Yet it did! At a temperature of 4.12° K, the electrical resistance of mercury completely vanished, or at least came so close to zero that no one has ever managed to measure any tiny trace of resistance that may be left. With no resistance, the mercury could conduct an electric current without any work required to keep the current going. (It was like sliding on infinitely smooth ice; you just keep sliding forever.) A current set up in a ring of mercury below 4.12° K will continue circling that ring indefinitely. This phenomenon is called *superconductivity*.

Since 1911, a number of other metals have been shown to become superconductive when a sufficiently low temperature is reached. Some require temperatures less than 1° K. For instance, iridium becomes superconductive only at temperatures less than 0.12° K. (Oddly enough, those metals that, at ordinary temperatures, are the best conductors—copper, silver, gold, aluminum—have shown no trace of superconductivity at the lowest temperatures at which they have been tested.)

A few metals remain superconductive at rather high temperatures. Lanthanum is superconductive up to 5.9° K and niobium up to 9.2° K. The record high temperature at which any known element is superconductive is 11.2° K for technetium. Unfortunately, technetium is a radioactive metal and has no stable isotopes. It does not occur in nature in appreciable quantities and must be synthesized in the laboratory. Therefore it will always be a rare substance.

Superconductivity also involves an odd property with respect to a magnetic field. There are some substances that are *diamagnetic*, that is, they seem to repel magnetic lines of force. Fewer lines of force will pass through such substances than through an equivalent volume of vacuum. In 1933, it was discovered that any superconductive substance was perfectly diamagnetic; no lines of force enter it at all.

If a magnetic field is made strong enough, however, some lines of force eventually manage to penetrate the diamagnetic substance, and superconductivity vanishes. In other words, for any given substance, superconductivity can be made to disappear by raising the temperature or the magnetic-field intensity above certain values. The higher one factor is raised, the less the other factor need be raised.

In the 1950's and 1960's strenuous efforts have been made to put the phenomenon of superconductivity to use. An electric current always produces a magnetic field, but, under ordinary circumstances, it requires a good deal of energy to keep a current going. To keep one going that is large enough to produce a really intense field takes enormous energies. The existence of superconductivity, however, raises the possibility of starting a large electric current that can continue flowing without any further input of energy. This will, in turn, produce an intense magnetic field that will remain in being without any energy input.

There is a limit, however, to how strong a magnetic field can be set up before magnetic lines of force penetrate the superconductor and end the phenomenon. Usually, this limit is unsatisfactorily low, but physicists have labored to find materials that will withstand as intense a magnetic field as possible. Magnets are now produced at liquid-helium temperatures that are unprecedentedly more powerful than anything in existence at ordinary temperatures.

The phenomenon of superconductivity has also made possible the invention of a tiny device that can act as a switch. In its simplest form, it consists of a small wire of tantalum wrapped about a wire of niobium. If the wires are dipped in liquid helium, the niobium wire becomes superconductive and a tiny current passed through it will remain in being indefinitely. When a current is then sent through the tantalum wire, the magnetic field set up about it is sufficient to disrupt the superconductivity and stop the current in the niobium.

Properly manipulated, such a device, called a *cryotron* (first devised in 1956), can be used to replace a vacuum tube or a transistor. Tiny devices, consisting of short, hairlike cryotrons, astutely arranged, can replace large numbers of bulky tubes or moderately bulky transistors, so that a giant computing machine of the future may well be desk-size or less if it is entirely "cryotronized."

These modern magnets and switches, however, can perform their wonders only at liquid-helium temperatures and helium is in limited supply. So much helium is now required in scientific research and in advanced devices of conceivable use to the space effort and to military affairs that helium production has increased tenfold and more since 1950; 90 per cent of the supply is now earmarked for various governmental agencies. What will happen when the gas wells that supply helium in large quantities run out, as they must do within a century?

In one respect, the helium we use is not lost. As in the case of argon, it enters the atmosphere. However, the atmospheric supply of helium is much smaller than that of argon; a large plant engaged in the fractional distillation of air can produce only 1 cubic foot of helium for every 2,000 produced from gas wells. Furthermore, the argon supply of the atmosphere is permanent, but not so the helium supply. Earth cannot hold helium and it slowly leaks out of the atmosphere and into space.

Yet helium is likely to grow more and more necessary to our advancing technology. One way of staving off the evil days of dwindling supply is to make use of the helium that we now waste. The United States (which owns most of the world's helium supply) produces it to the extent of over 10,000,000,000 (10 billion) liters a year; and the potential is considerably higher. It is estimated that each year over 100,000,000,000 (100 billion) liters are left in natural gas and allowed to escape into the atmosphere when the gas is burned. If this helium could be recovered, we would have the gas in good supply for ten times as long, perhaps, as we would otherwise.

One way of making do, even without helium, would be to discover methods of maintaining superconductivity at liquid-hydrogen temperatures, since liquid hydrogen is in virtually limitless supply.

Since solid hydrogen does not melt until a temperature of 14° K is reached, such a temperature is a minimum requirement for liquid-hydrogen superconductivity. No element is superconductive at so high a temperature, but some alloys are. An alloy of niobium and tin is superconductive at a temperature as high as 18.1° K.

Niobium-tin can be kept superconductive in liquid hydrogen, then, provided liquid hydrogen is kept a couple of degrees below its boiling point, which is difficult to manage without liquid helium. If we could establish superconductivity above 20° K, the boiling point of hydrogen, then superconductivity could be maintained easily in liquid hydrogen.

Materials with superconductivity at temperatures above 20° K have not yet been located, although there are suggestions that through the use of special kinds of large organic molecules, rather similar to those that occur in living tissue, superconductivity may become possible even at room temperature. If that were so, it would bring about a monumental revolution in technology. However, this remains, as yet, strictly in the realm of speculation.

8

The Inertness of Noble Gases

Clathrate Compounds

From the moment of the discovery of the noble gases, the property of inertness—the failure to react with other substances—was unmistakable. Cavendish's final bubble of air was there because the gas that made it up refused to combine with oxygen. When Rayleigh and Ramsay finally isolated and studied Cavendish's gas, they called it argon ("inert") because that was its most prominent characteristic.

"Inert," however, does not necessarily mean "completely inert." Nitrogen is an inert gas; for instance, in the heat of a forest fire in which a myriad of substances are combining violently with oxygen, nothing combines with the nitrogen of the atmosphere. And yet nitrogen is not completely inert. The lightning bolt will supply the energies to force nitrogen and oxygen into union; man can duplicate that effect on a small scale in the laboratory. Nitrogen will even combine quite easily with some metals such as magnesium and calcium.

There was no question that all the noble gases were more inert than nitrogen and even less apt to combine with other substances. But were even the noble gases, although clearly the most inert of all elements, completely inert? There was considerable evidence that they were not, in fact, completely inert.

If the noble gases were completely inert, there would be no attraction at all between their atoms and any others; not even between one noble gas atom and another like itself. With no interatomic attraction at all, noble gases would remain gaseous down to absolute zero; none of them do that. All become liquid when the temperature is low enough. The more complex the noble-gas atom the higher is its liquefaction point (see Table 28, Chapter 7), but even helium, with the smallest of the noble-gas atoms and, apparently, possessing the least interatomic attraction, finally liquefies.

Inertness, then, is not absolute. If we judge by the liquefaction point, the more complex the noble-gas atom, the less inert it is. On that basis, radon is the least inert of the noble gases* and helium is the most inert.

Another indication that the noble gases are not completely inert is that they are soluble to some extent in water. If they were completely inert, there would be no attraction between their atoms and water molecules and there would be no forces present to bring about solution. Yet there is solubility to a certain extent (see Table 26, Chapter 7), and this, too, is an indication that inertness is not absolute. Radon is the most

---

* In actual fact, the rare and radioactive radon is so difficult to work with that it is almost always disregarded in such chemical questions. It is usually taken, then, that xenon, the second heaviest noble gas, and the heaviest *stable* noble gas, is the least inert in a practical sense.

soluble of the noble gases; the solubility decreases as the atomic weight grows smaller, until we reach helium, which is the least soluble. Again, we can conclude that radon is the least inert of the noble gases and helium the most inert.

Thus, if the noble-gas atoms show enough attraction for water molecules to go into solution to some extent, might they not show enough attraction to join them in a compound under some circumstances? And might this not show up in clearest fashion among the heavier inert gases, which are more soluble and therefore attract water molecules more strongly?

In the early years after the discovery of the noble gases, chemists tried to bring about such compound formation by increasing the attractive forces between the noble-gas atoms and the water molecules still further. They did this by mixing a noble gas with water under pressure. The atoms and molecules, crowded into closer quarters, so to speak, could possibly find it easier to combine.

This proved to be the case, but only for the heavier noble gases—argon, krypton, and xenon. Individual atoms of each seemed to form a union with six water molecules, producing *noble-gas hydrates* as solid crystals. We can present the formulas of these as $Ar(H_2O)_6$, $Kr(H_2O)_6$, and $Xe(H_2O)_6$. The first of these was produced as early as 1896, by the French chemist P. Villard. Undoubtedly, radon could also form the hydrate, $Rn(H_2O)_6$, if it were not so difficult to attempt to work with radon. The noble-gas hydrates are not stable substances, but break apart rapidly as the pressure that originally brought about their formation is removed.

As expected, of the noble-gas hydrates, *argon hydrate* is the most difficult to form and breaks up most easily. *Krypton hydrate* requires less pressure to form and less pressure to keep from breaking up; and *xenon hydrate* requires still less. Xenon hydrate is almost stable at ordinary pressure, and *radon hydrate,* if it were formed, would surely prove to be stable at ordinary .

pressures. This is in line with the other evidence that inertness decreases as atomic weight rises. It is also not surprising that neon and helium, the most inert of the inert gases, so far have not been forced into hydrate formation at any pressure.

As time went on, it was shown that argon, krypton, and xenon (but never neon and helium) also formed combinations with molecules more complex than those of water. A substance called "hydroquinone" was a good example. For that matter, it was discovered in 1965 that xenon would form combinations with hemoglobin.

All these combinations, however, proved to be false alarms in a sense. In 1949 it was shown that hydroquinone molecules could combine loosely with each other, end-to-end. A number of such molecules could combine in this way to form a three-dimensional cagelike structure, possessing a hollow interior in which an atom or small molecule could be trapped if it happened to be present in the right spot while the structure was forming. In short, hydroquinone forms a kind of cage within which an atom of noble gas can play the part of a canary. Water molecules can also build up such a cage and similarly hold a noble-gas atom.

A substance formed by the entrapment of an atom or molecule within a cagelike structure is called a *clathrate compound* from a Latin word meaning "caged in." All the substances discovered to incorporate noble-gas atoms during the first half of the twentieth century turned out to be clathrate compounds.

Clathrate compounds are not true compounds of the ordinary type. An argon atom is not bound to hydroquinone by a chemical bond, but is physically trapped within the cage. When the cage breaks apart (and it holds together but loosely), the argon escapes at once. That is the reason why argon hydrate breaks up so readily. When the pressure is removed, the cage breaks.

Nevertheless, the existence of the clathrate compounds

shows the manner in which inertness decreases as the noble-gas atom becomes more complex. There should be a feeble attraction between the noble-gas atom and the molecule of water or of hydroquinone, if the noble-gas atom is to be kept in place for the split second during which the cage is built up.

The attraction is so small in the case of helium and neon that neither of these atoms will stay put long enough to allow the cage to be built around them. Hence, they form no clathrate compounds. Argon atoms with somewhat stronger attraction for other molecules can be trapped; krypton with still stronger attraction can be trapped more easily; and xenon still more easily.

Again, when a clathrate cage momentarily opens up, the enclosed atom may stay put long enough to allow the cage to re-form. It then does not escape. The weaker the attractive force, the more likely the escape of the enclosed atom before re-formation of the cage. Hence, the clathrate compounds of argon, once formed, are less stable than those of krypton, which are, in turn, less stable than those of xenon.

Ionization Potential

Clathrate compounds are quite unsatisfactory as evidence of chemical activity of the noble gases. The formation of a clathrate compound involves only those very feeble attractions between one atom and the next that cause a noble gas to become a liquid if the temperature is dropped low enough; or that cause it to dissolve slightly in water.

The question is: Can noble-gas atoms form an "ordinary" compound, and be incorporated into "ordinary" molecules, in the same fashion that hydrogen atoms, for instance, combine with oxygen atoms to form molecules of water?

If one were guided by the earliest notions of valence (the notions that helped Mendeléev devise the periodic table), one might conclude that the answer was "no"; that the noble gases could not form compounds because they were in a column headed "valence 0."

By the time the noble gases were discovered, however, chemists knew very well that the rules of valence were not so rigid as the periodic table made it appear. Some elements showed variable valence, for instance. Carbon formed some compounds in which its valence was 2 rather than 4. Gold formed a series of compounds in which it exhibited a valence of 1, and another series in which it exhibited a valence of 3. Manganese atoms, in one compound or another, exhibited valences of 2, 3, 4, 6, and 7.

It became apparent that atomic behavior was not really simple and that the noble-gas atoms, although ordinarily possessing a valence of 0, and ordinarily not forming compounds, might show a valence other than 0 under exceptional circumstances. Many chemists investigated the matter on various occasions. A number of noble-gas compounds were reported as having been prepared at one time or another, but such reports were always shown to be mistaken, right down to the 1960's.

As the twentieth century progressed and the structure of the atom came to be better understood, chemists began to interpret valence, and the ability of one atom to combine with another, in terms of electrons. This made it possible to approach the question of noble-gas compounds in a more systematic fashion.

To begin with, an "ordinary" compound is formed when there are actual electron transfers; when one atom gives up (in whole or in part) one or more electrons, while the other atom accepts (in whole or in part) one or more electrons. In the case of the water molecule (H_2O), each hydrogen atom, for instance, gives up most of its grip on its single electron, while the single oxygen atom accepts the lion's share of the grip on both.

Of the 103 known elements, only about eight have a really strong tendency to accept additional electrons. These elements, among which oxygen and chlorine are prominent, almost invariably appear in molecules in their role as electron-acceptors. Another eight elements (notably, carbon and hydrogen) can both accept and donate electrons and can appear in molecules in either role. Then, there are six elements (the noble gases) that neither accept nor donate electrons under ordinary circumstances and do not readily participate in molecule formation at all. That leaves some 80 elements that are primarily electron-donors; they appear in that role in molecule production.

In 1914, two German physicists, James Franck (1882–1964) and Gustav Hertz (b. 1887), evolved a method for measuring the ease with which the atoms of a particular element could be made to give up electrons. Essentially, they hurled a stream of electrons through a thin scattering of atoms of the element being investigated. Ordinarily, the electrons simply bounce off the atoms.

As the electron potential driving the electrons increases, however, the electrons gain more and more energy; eventually, they strike the atoms so hard as to shake loose an electron from the atom. When this happens, the original moving electrons lose much of their energy, for it is consumed in shaking loose the atom's electron. It is the point of energy loss for which the experimenter is watching.

Once an atom loses an electron, what is left of the atom carries a positive charge and becomes an ion. The electric potential at which the stream of electrons suddenly loses energy (indicating that an ion has been formed) is therefore called the *ionization potential* of the element. Electric potential is measured in units called *volts*, and the ionization potential is therefore customarily given in volts.

For instance, a stream of electrons moving under an electric potential of 13.60 volts is just energetic enough to knock loose the single electron of the hydrogen atom. Therefore, the ionization potential of hydrogen is 13.60 volts.

The ionization potential varies according to the electronic structure of the atom. Consider the sodium atom, for instance. It possesses a nucleus with a positive charge of $+11$; circling that nucleus are eleven electrons, each with a charge of -1, so that the atom, taken as a whole, is electrically neutral.

The eleven electrons of the sodium atom are arranged $2/8/1$ (see Page 65). The two electrons of the innermost shell are most strongly attracted to the nucleus. For one thing, they may be pictured as being closest to the nucleus, and the attractive force between positive and negative charges increases as the distance between them decreases.

The eight electrons of the middle shell are less strongly held. They are farther from the nucleus than the innermost two electrons, so that the attraction of the positive charge of the nucleus is weakened for that reason. Then, too, the two electrons in the innermost shell tend to shield some of the positive charge of the nucleus. To put it another way, like electric charges repel each other, and the eight electrons of the middle shell, while attracted by the positive charge of the nucleus, are also somewhat repelled by the negative charge of the two inner electrons that lie between them and the nucleus. That further cuts down the force with which the middle shell is held in place.

The single electron in the outermost shell is held most weakly of all. Not only is it much farther from the nucleus than the remaining electrons; it is also shielded off from the nucleus by the repulsion of no less than ten negatively charged electrons lying between itself and the nucleus. The outermost electron of the sodium atom is therefore so weakly held as to be easily removed. In fact, the ionization potential is but 5.12 volts, less than half that of hydrogen.

If sodium atoms are bombarded with still more energetic

electrons, a second electron may be broken loose. However, this second electron would have to come from the middle shell of eight electrons, which are much more strongly held by the nucleus. Indeed, a second electron is not removed from the sodium atoms until a potential of 47.06 volts is reached.

Each time an electron is removed from an atom, the remaining electrons seem to draw in more closely to the nucleus and it becomes that much harder to pull an additional electron away. A third electron is not pulled loose from the sodium atom until a potential of 70.72 volts is reached.

We can say, therefore, that, for the sodium atom, ionization potential (I) $= 5.2$ volts; ionization potential (II) $= 47.06$ volts; and ionization potential (III) $= 70.72$ volts.

An atom that has a tendency to attract electrons can easily pull away one of the electrons of the sodium atom against that atom's feeble attraction. No atom has so strong an attraction for electrons, however, as to be able to pull away a second or a third electron from sodium. In consequence, in all chemical reactions, sodium gives up a single electron, no more, and has what we call a valence of 1.

Next, let us consider the magnesium atom, which has a nucleus with a positive charge of $+ 12$, and twelve circling electrons with an arrangement of 2/8/2. The situation here is similar to that in sodium. The two outermost electrons, which are most distant from the positively charged nucleus and which are separated from that nucleus by the largest number of negatively charged electrons, are the most feebly held. Those outermost electrons are, nevertheless, held more firmly by the magnesium nucleus than was the case for sodium. The outermost electrons of the magnesium atom are also shielded by ten inner electrons, but they are attracted by a positive charge of $+ 12$, not $+ 11$ as in the case of sodium. Consequently, ionization potential (I) of magnesium is 7.61 volts, about half again as high as is that of sodium.

Once the first electron of magnesium is removed, the other outermost electron is held more firmly, and ionization potential (II) is 14.96 volts. To remove a third electron from magnesium, however, requires reaching into the middle shell and that is much more difficult, so that ionization potential (III) of magnesium is 79.72.

Atoms capable of accepting electrons can therefore drag the first two electrons away from the magnesium atom, but cannot touch the third. In all chemical reactions, then, the magnesium atom gives up two electrons, and no more. It has a valence of 2.

For some atoms, the ionization potentials are spaced in such a way as to make it possible to withdraw sometimes one electron and sometimes two; or sometimes one and sometimes three; or sometimes two and sometimes three, and so on. This accounts for variable valence. Usually, there is one particular valence that is displayed most characteristically; generally, it is the one that belongs to the column of the periodic table in which the element is found.

For our purposes, we need only consider the first ionization potential of any element—the potential required to remove the first electron. It will be to this that I refer when I speak simply of the "ionization potential" without making use of any Roman numerals.

The lower this ionization potential, the more easily does an element give up at least one of its electrons, and the more readily does it take part in compound formation.

When we are dealing with a group of elements with the same number of electron shells in the atom, the ionization potential tends to go up as the number of electrons in the outermost shell increases—for the charge on the nucleus increases and the electrons in the outermost shell are held progressively more firmly. It is for this reason, for instance, that the ionization potential of magnesium is higher than that of sodium.

On the whole, then, in any row of elements, the one whose atoms contain a single electron in the outermost shell takes part most actively in those processes that involve the giving up of electrons. The atoms with but one electron in their outermost shell are the alkali metals (see Page 65) and the alkali metals are therefore the most active of all electron-donating elements.

How do the alkali metals differ among themselves? Suppose we compare sodium with potassium. Where the sodium atom has a nucleus with a charge of $+ 11$ and eleven electrons arranged 2/8/1, the potassium atom has a nucleus with a charge of $+ 19$ and nineteen electrons arranged 2/8/8/1.

The outermost electron of the potassium atom is attracted by a more highly charged nucleus than that of the sodium atom. On the other hand, the outermost electron of the potassium atom is more distant from its nucleus than that of the sodium atom, and is separated from that nucleus by a larger number of electrons. On the whole, the effect of greater charge on the nucleus is more than counterbalanced by the greater distance and greater number of intervening electrons. Consequently, the ionization potential of potassium is less than that of sodium: 4.318 volts as compared with 5.12 volts.

In fact, if we list the ionization potentials for all the alkali metals, as in Table 30, we can see how the value decreases

Table 30. Ionization Potentials of the Alkali Metals

Alkali Metal	Nuclear Charge	Electron Arrangement	Ionization Potential (Volts)
Lithium	$+ 3$	2/1	5.363
Sodium	$+ 11$	2/8/1	5.12
Potassium	$+ 19$	2/8/8/1	4.318
Rubidium	$+ 37$	2/8/18/8/1	4.159
Cesium	$+ 55$	2/8/18/18/8/1	3.87
Francium	$+ 87$	2/8/18/32/18/8/1	?

regularly with the increasing complexity of the atom. (Only francium does not have its ionization potential listed in the table. It is a radioactive element with a very short half-life, and it is very difficult to study its properties, so that its ionization potential is, as yet, unknown. However, it is quite safe to suppose that its ionization potential is less than 3.87 volts.)

Of the stable elements involved in electron-donating processes, we can conclude that the alkali metals are the most active, and that cesium is the most active of the stable alkali metals.

Ionization Potentials of the Noble Gases

When we turn to the noble gases, we are at the opposite pole. As the number of electrons in the outermost shell rises, the ionization potential does too. Since the maximum number of electrons in the outermost shell of any atom is eight (except for helium, where it is two), we can expect the ionization potential to be at a peak in those cases. The atoms with eight electrons in the outermost shell are those of the noble gases; indeed, they, as a group, have less tendency to give up electrons than any other group of elements.

Yet the ionization potential has a definite value even for the noble-gas atoms; electrons can be broken away from them. The ionization potential of argon, for instance, is 15.68 volts. This is three times as high as that of sodium, but it is not very much higher than that of hydrogen.

Furthermore, the rule that the more complex the atom of a given family, the lower the ionization potential holds for the noble gases, too, as we can see from Table 31.

From the ionization potentials, as from liquefaction points and solubilities, we can see that the more complex the noble-gas atom, the less inert it must be.

Indeed, judging from ionization potentials alone, we might

conclude that the heavier noble gases are not inert at all. The ionization potentials of xenon and radon are distinctly less than that of hydrogen, while the ionization potential of krypton is just a trifle higher. Might it not follow from this that these three gases ought to give up electrons and form compounds as easily as hydrogen, or even more easily? Unfortunately, no. The trouble is that ionization potentials are not the only deciding factors in estimating the activity of an element.

Consider, for a moment, hydrogen and nitrogen. The ionization potential of hydrogen is 13.527; that of nitrogen is 14.48. One would expect then that nitrogen might have a lesser tendency to give up electrons than hydrogen, but not much less. Since hydrogen gives up electrons to oxygen quite easily to form water molecules (H_2O), should not nitrogen give up electrons to oxygen to form molecules of nitrogen oxide (NO), with less ease perhaps, but not necessarily with much less ease? Apparently not. Nitrogen combines with oxygen only with the greatest difficulty.

There are two reasons for this. In the first place, hydrogen, nitrogen, and oxygen all exist as diatomic molecules and in order to interact at least a small fraction of those molecules should first be broken down to single atoms. Of the three molecules, the hydrogen molecule is the easiest to decompose. The nitrogen

Table 31. Ionization Potentials of the Noble Gases

Noble Gas	Nuclear Charge	Electron Arrangement	Ionization Potential (Volts)
Helium	$+2$	2	24.46
Neon	$+10$	2/8	21.47
Argon	$+18$	2/8/8	15.68
Krypton	$+36$	2/8/18/8	13.93
Xenon	$+54$	2/8/18/18/8	12.08
Radon	$+86$	2/8/18/32/18/8	10.70

molecule is held together much more firmly and breaks apart to individual atoms to a much smaller degree than hydrogen does; therefore, one would expect nitrogen to react more sluggishly than hydrogen for that reason only, and regardless of the ionization potential.

Furthermore, in passing from a mixture of hydrogen and oxygen to water, we are passing from a condition of lesser stability to one of greater stability, and a great deal of energy is liberated. This energy serves to raise the temperature of the remaining hydrogen and oxygen, breaking apart still more of the hydrogen molecules into individual atoms, and hastening the reaction, which in turn raises the temperature still further. For that reason, if a mixture of hydrogen and oxygen is heated to the point where the reaction reaches a certain critical rate, the temperature zooms, and the entire mixture explodes. A temperature of about 525° C is enough to turn the trick.

When a mixture of nitrogen and oxygen is converted to nitrogen oxide, however, a condition of greater stability is being converted to one of less stability. Heat is absorbed in the course of the reaction so that the temperature tends to drop—stopping the reaction, rather than hastening it. Consequently, even when enough energy is added to air as to cause nitrogen and oxygen to begin combining (as in the neighborhood of a lightning bolt), the reaction does not build up to an explosion of the earth's atmosphere. Rather, it damps out almost at once.

Here is another case. The ionization potential (I) and (II) of magnesium are 7.61 volts and 14.96 volts, respectively. When magnesium is heated in air, its atoms combine vigorously with those of oxygen to form magnesium oxide (MgO). Each oxygen atom pulls two electrons away from a magnesium atom, even though the second electron requires 14.96 volts for removal.

Under similar conditions, oxygen atoms will not touch krypton atoms, although the first electron can be pulled away at a potential of only 13.93 volts. Again, it is a matter of whether or not the change is in the direction of greater stability. When two electrons leave the magnesium atom, the ten electrons left have the stable 2/8 arrangement. Magnesium, in reacting with oxygen, is therefore passing from an electronic configuration of lesser stability to one of greater. In the case of the krypton atom, the loss of one electron would bring about a change from a 2/8/18/8 arrangement to one of 2/8/18/7. The change would be from greater to lesser stability. We can therefore compare the oxidation of magnesium to that of hydrogen, and the oxidation of krypton to that of nitrogen.

If we are to compare the noble gases to other elements on the basis of ionization potential, we must find cases where the loss of an electron brings about a configuration of lesser stability, and where there are no extraneous energy conditions to encourage reaction.

A possible example is the oxygen atom itself. The oxygen atom has a strong tendency to accept electrons; it is for this reason that oxygen is an active element. However, the oxygen atom also has a tendency (a much smaller one) to give up electrons, and it is this electron-donating tendency we must consider. The oxygen atom has eight electrons, arranged 2/6. The ionization potential of oxygen is 13.550, which is distinctly higher than that of xenon and only a trifle below that of krypton. Furthermore, when an oxygen atom loses an electron, the configuration of those remaining is 2/5, a condition of no particular stability, so that oxygen has no advantage over krypton and xenon in this respect.

Of course, gaseous xenon and krypton exist in single atoms, while oxygen exists in two-atom molecules. Does this complicate matters? It might, but to see if it does, we need only consider the ionization potential of the oxygen molecule. An electron can be pulled out of one of the atoms of the oxygen molecule without breaking the connection between the atoms.

It turns out that the ionization potential of the oxygen molecule is somewhat lower than that of the oxygen atom. It is 12.11 volts, which is almost exactly that of xenon.

It follows, then, that oxygen (in its electron-donating tendency) is quite comparable to the heavier noble gases. By keeping an eye on oxygen, we may be guided to the production of noble-gas compounds, if any exist.

Electron-Accepting Atoms

If we are going to consider conditions under which electrons can be pulled away from atoms such as oxygen and xenon, which do not readily give up electrons, we must expect those conditions to be extreme. In chemical reactions, one or more electrons are pulled away from particular atoms only because some other atom is capable of accepting one or more electrons. Only a very strong electron-acceptor could be expected to make a dent on an oxygen or xenon atom.

The atoms that have the strongest tendency to accept electrons are those without outermost shells containing nearly eight electrons. By accepting one or two electrons, they would build up the stable configuration of eight outer electrons, and the tendency to do so is great.

The group of elements with seven electrons in the outermost shell (the halogens) need accept only one electron to make up the stable number and are therefore the most active in participating in those chemical processes involving the acceptance of electrons. These elements (see Table 18, Chapter 4) are, in order of increasing atomic complexity: fluorine, chlorine, bromine, iodine, and astatine.

As I have already explained, the more complex the atom of a particular group, the more weakly it holds its outermost electrons, and, therefore, the weaker is its tendency to attract additional electrons. It follows that the smaller the halogen atom, the more strongly it holds its outermost electrons, and the greater its tendency to accept an additional electron. In other words, iodine will accept an electron more readily than astatine. Bromine will accept one still more readily; chlorine more readily yet; and fluorine most readily of all.

Those elements with six electrons in the outermost shell are also active in accepting electrons, though not so active (as a group) as are the halogens. Here, too, the smaller the atom the more readily it will accept an electron, so that the second smallest (sulfur) is fairly active, and the smallest (oxygen) is quite active.

Elements with five electrons in the outermost shell are less active still, but the smallest atom of that group (nitrogen) makes a respectable showing.

The American chemist Linus Pauling (b. 1901) considered the electron-accepting properties (*electronegativity*) of the atoms in detail. In 1932, he applied the mathematical treatment of atomic structure, developed in the previous decade, to the problem of electron transfer; on that basis he worked out a measure of the electronegativity of the various elements. In Table 32, the seven most electronegative elements (in order of decreasing electronegativity) are listed in accordance with Pauling's scale.

Table 32. The Most Electronegative Elements

Element	Electron Arrangement	Electronegativity (Pauling's Scale)
Fluorine	2/7	4.0
Oxygen	2/6	3.5
Chlorine	2/8/7	3.0
Nitrogen	2/5	3.0
Bromine	2/8/18/7	2.8
Sulfur	2/8/6	2.5
Iodine	2/8/18/18/7	2.5

The order given in Table 32 holds, strictly speaking, for the individual atoms of these elements. When the elements exist as molecules, their activity is affected by the ease with which those molecules can be broken down to individual atoms.

The oxygen molecule (O_2) holds together more firmly than do the diatomic molecules of the various halogens. The nitrogen molecule (N_2) holds together more firmly still. For this reason, oxygen is not very active at room temperature despite its position on the electronegativity list. We can live comfortably under an ocean of oxygen without being bothered, though our body tissues would quickly combine with the less electronegative bromine. As for nitrogen, it remains an inert gas even at elevated temperatures.

Whether we consider atoms or molecules, then, fluorine is, beyond question, the most active of all the elements in accepting electrons. Indeed, if fluorine cannot force electrons away from the atom of some particular element, then no other substance can.

If any of the noble gases can be made to give up an electron or two and form a compound, it can most easily do so with fluorine. Let us turn our attention to fluorine, then.

9

Fluorine

The Recognition of Fluorine

Actually, Pauling's mathematical treatment of electronegativity was not needed to convince chemists of fluorine's unusual activity. It merely confirmed what had been suspected for at least a century, as a result of practical laboratory experience in the course of fluorine's tragic history.

This history begins with the miners of early modern times. In 1529, the German mineralogist George Agricola (1490–1555) described the uses of a certain mineral in ore-smelting. The mineral itself melted easily, for a mineral, and, when added to the ore being smelted in a furnace, caused it to melt more easily, thus bringing about a valuable saving of fuel and time.

Agricola called the mineral *fluores* from the Latin word meaning "to flow," because it liquefied and flowed so easily. In later years, it came to be called *fluorspar*, since *spar* is an old German word for a mineral; a still newer name is *fluorite*, since "ite" is now the conventional suffix used to denote a mineral.*

In 1670, a German glass cutter, Heinrich Schwanhard, found that when he treated fluorspar with strong acid, a vapor was produced that etched his spectacles. This was most unusual, for glass is generally unaffected by chemicals, even by strong ones. Schwanhard took advantage of this property to develop a new art form. He covered portions of glassware with protective varnish and exposed it to the vapor, ending with clear figures on a cloudy background. Naturally, Schwanhard did not know the chemical details of what was happening, but the process of etching was dramatic enough, and the art work he produced was unusual enough to attract continuing interest.

The Swedish chemist Karl Wilhelm Scheele (1741–1786) was the first to study the vapor of acidified fluorspar in some detail, in 1771. He was able to show, for instance, that the vapor was an acid, and he called it "fluoric acid." As a result, Scheele is commonly given credit for having discovered the substance.

It was probably a tragic discovery, for Scheele had a bad habit of sniffing and tasting any new substances he discovered. "Fluoric acid" was one of several of his discoveries that most definitely should not be treated in this manner. He died at the early age of forty-four, after some years of invalidism; in all probability, his habit of sniffing and sipping unknown chemicals drastically shortened his life. If so, "fluoric acid" (and other chemicals) had its first famous chemical victim. Scheele was by no means the last.

Once Scheele had established that the vapor produced from acidified fluorspar was an acid, a misconception at once arose as to its structure. The great French chemist Antoine Laurent

---

* Fluorspar, or fluorite, gives off a bluish color when exposed to ultraviolet light. This production of visible light under the influence of ultraviolet is exhibited by many substances, but it is fluorspar that gave the phenomenon its name—fluorescence.

Lavoisier had decided at just that time that all acids contained oxygen, and it was difficult to break away from that view in the face of so famous a proponent.

In 1810, however, the English chemist Humphry Davy (1778–1829) was able to show that "muriatic acid," a well-known strong acid, contained no oxygen. He decided that a green gas that could be obtained from muriatic acid was an element; he named it "chlorine" from a Greek word for "green." "Muriatic acid" then was a compound, Davy demonstrated, of hydrogen and chlorine—but no oxygen—and could be called *hydrogen chloride* in its gaseous state, or *hydrochloric acid*, when dissolved in water.

By 1813, Davy was convinced that Scheele's "fluoric acid" was another example of an acid without oxygen. The French physicist, André Marie Ampère, suggested that the molecule consisted of hydrogen plus an unknown element. Since "fluoric acid" had certain similarities to the newly renamed hydrochloric acid, it seemed very likely to both Davy and Ampère that the unknown element was very like chlorine. Indeed, they decided to call it *fluorine;* the first syllable coming from "fluorspar," while the suffix was chosen to emphasize the similarity of the new element to chlorine. "Fluoric acid" became *hydrogen fluoride* in its gaseous form; *hydrofluoric acid* in solution.

The Isolation of Fluorine

What chemists wanted to do, once the existence of fluorine came to be so strongly suspected, was to settle all doubts by isolating the element.

Hydrogen chloride (HCl) could, after all, be treated with oxygen-containing chemicals in such a way that the hydrogen atom was snatched away and attached to oxygen to form water. The chlorine atoms, left behind, combined to form chlorine molecules (Cl_2).

Could not hydrogen fluoride (HF) be similarly treated, so

that molecular fluorine (F_2) would be formed? Unfortunately, it could not. As we now know, oxygen is more electronegative than chlorine and can snatch hydrogen's electron (along with the rest of the hydrogen atom) from chlorine. Oxygen is, however, less electronegative than fluorine and is helpless to remove hydrogen from the hydrogen fluoride molecule.

Indeed, as no chemical reactions sufficed to liberate fluorine gas from its compounds, it became clear to nineteenth-century chemists that fluorine atoms held on to the atoms of other elements with record strength. Once free, those same fluorine atoms would recombine with other atoms with immense vigor. It came to be suspected, therefore, that fluorine was the most active of all elements (long before Pauling demonstrated it by means of his carefully worked-out theories) and the most difficult to liberate. That, of course, made the task of liberation all the more of a challenge.

Davy himself had shown that it was not necessary to use chemical reactions in order to liberate a particular element from its compounds. An electric current, passing through a molten compound, can, under proper circumstances, separate the elements composing the compound. He demonstrated this in the case of the alkali metals and alkaline earth metals. The atoms of these elements are the most active in giving up electrons, and they therefore form compounds readily and are released from those compounds only with great difficulty. Prior to Davy's time, these elements had not been isolated, but in 1807 and 1808, using an electric current, Davy isolated and named six metals: sodium, potassium, magnesium, calcium, strontium, and barium.

It seemed natural that fluorine-containing compounds could be split up and free fluorine gas liberated by some electrical method; beginning with Davy, chemist after chemist tried. The attempts were dangerous in the extreme, for hydrogen fluoride is a very poisonous gas and free fluorine, once liberated, is more poisonous still. Davy was badly poisoned by breathing small quantities of hydrogen fluoride and this may have contributed to his later invalidism and his death at the age of only fifty-one.

Other prominent chemists of the time were also poisoned, and their lives made miserable and undoubtedly shortened by the same source. One notable Belgian chemist, Paulin Louyet, was actually killed, as was the French chemist Jérôme Nicklès. And yet the danger of the work seemed but to add to the challenge and excitement of the problem.

The usual starting substance in the attempt to obtain fluorine was fluorspar, which by the nineteenth century was understood to be *calcium fluoride* (CaF_2). To pass an electric current through fluorspar, one had to melt it first and then maintain it at a comparatively high temperature throughout the experiment. Fluorine was more active than ever at such high temperatures.

It was probably formed by the current, but as soon as it was, it promptly attacked everything in sight. It corroded the electrodes through which the electric current entered the fluorspar, even when they were composed of such comparatively inert materials as carbon, silver—even platinum.

A French chemist, Edmond Frémy (1814–1894), a student of the martyred Louyet, repeated the work with fluorspar in 1855, with the usual unsatisfactory results. It occurred to him that it might be preferable to pass an electric current through hydrogen fluoride. Hydrogen fluoride was a liquid at room temperature, and at this lower temperature, fluorine might be easier to handle. Unfortunately, until Frémy's time, hydrogen fluoride was available only in water solution. If there was any water about, fluorine reacted with it at once, tearing the hydrogen atoms out of the water molecule with such force that oxygen was liberated in the energetic form of ozone. One ended with hydrogen fluoride again.

Frémy therefore worked out methods for producing *anhydrous hydrogen fluoride*, that is, hydrogen fluoride that was pure and water-free, by acidifying potassium hydrogen fluoride

(KHF_2). Unfortunately, he found himself stymied. Anhydrous hydrogen fluoride would not pass an electric current.

In the end, he, too, gave up. As the 1880's dawned, fluorine was still victor. It had defeated the best efforts of many first-class chemists for three quarters of a century. (But Frémy, at least, took sufficient care of himself in the course of his experiments to live to be eighty—no mean feat for a fluorine chemist.)

Frémy had a student, Ferdinand Frédéric Henri Moissan, who took up the battle. He tried everything. He formed phosphorus trifluoride and tried to combine it with oxygen. Oxygen and phosphorus held together particularly tightly, and in this case, Moissan felt, the oxygen might be able to compete successfully with fluorine. Not entirely. The battle ended in a draw and Moissan ended with a compound in which phosphorus was combined with both oxygen and fluorine.

He then tried to pass phosphorus trifluoride over red-hot platinum. Platinum combines with fluorine only weakly and it also combines with phosphorus; perhaps it would combine only with the phosphorus and liberate the fluorine. No such luck. Both phosphorus and fluorine combined with the platinum.

Moissan decided to try electrical methods again. He began with arsenic fluoride and abandoned that after beginning to detect in himself signs of arsenic poisoning. He then turned to hydrogen fluoride, and eventually underwent four different episodes of poisoning with that gas, which undoubtedly helped cause his death at the age of fifty-four.

Moissan made use of Frémy's anhydrous hydrogen fluoride, but decided to add something to it to make it possible for it to carry an electric current. He had to add something that would not make it possible for some element other than fluorine to be liberated at the positive electrode. (If any element other than fluorine could be liberated, it would be—fluorine was last in line.) Moissan added potassium hydrogen fluoride to the hydrogen fluoride. The liquid was simply a mixture of fluorides and now it would carry a current.

Furthermore, Moissan made use of equipment built up out of an alloy of platinum and iridium, an alloy that was even more resistant to fluorine than platinum itself. Finally, he brought his entire apparatus to a temperature of $-50°$ C, where even fluorine's activity ought to be subdued.

And yet the experiment failed. Moissan considered and noted that the stoppers that held the electrodes had been corroded. Something was needed for the stopper that would not conduct a current, so the platinum-iridium alloy was eliminated. What else? It occurred to him that fluorspar itself did not carry a current, and could not be attacked by fluorine, either (it already held all the fluorine it could). Moissan carefully carved stoppers out of fluorspar and repeated the experiment.

On June 26, 1886, he obtained a pale yellow-green gas about the positive electrode. Fluorine had finally been isolated, and when Moissan later repeated the experiment in public, his old teacher, Frémy, watched.

Moissan went on, in 1899, to discover a less expensive way of producing fluorine. He made use of copper vessels. Fluorine attacked copper violently, but after the copper was overlaid with copper fluoride, no further attacks need be expected. In 1906, the year before his death, Moissan received the Nobel Prize in chemistry for his feat.

Despite all this, fluorine remained a most ticklish problem for another generation. It could be isolated and used, but not easily and not often. Most of all, it had to be handled with extreme care—and few chemists cared to play with it.

Pauling's Prediction

By the 1920's, fluorine was known to form compounds with every element on the list except the noble gases and oxygen. This was not surprising. The noble gases seemed completely inert, and although oxygen is very active, the nature of its activity clashed head-on with that of fluorine.

Fluorine and oxygen are the most electronegative elements on the list. The atoms of each accept electrons readily but do not readily give them up. To form a compound, the atoms of one would have to snatch at electrons that were being held tightly by the other.

In 1927, it was found that when fluorine was passed slowly through a solution of a compound called sodium hydroxide, a gas was obtained that smelled like fluorine and was almost as powerful a chemical as fluorine. However, it was not fluorine, for it was a colorless gas that liquefied at $-145°$ C, whereas fluorine was a pale yellow-green gas that liquefied at $-188°$ C.

On investigation, the gas proved to consist of molecules made up of two fluorine atoms and an oxygen atom; the formula is usually written F_2O. This compound is generally called "fluorine monoxide" simply because compounds of oxygen and one other element had always been called oxides in the past.

However, when oxygen combines with any element but fluorine, oxygen is the more electronegative of the two and it is the oxygen atom that accepts electrons at the expense of the other atoms concerned. The term oxide should be applied only to such compounds.

In the case of "fluorine monoxide," however, the oxygen atom does not accept the electrons. It cannot, for the fluorine atom is the one atom that has an even firmer grip on electrons than oxygen. Here it is the oxygen atom that gives up the electrons and the fluorine atom that accepts. Therefore, the compound should be called *oxygen fluoride*. In formulas, the symbols of the elements are usually written in the order of increasingly electronegative elements from left to right. The formula of oxygen fluoride ought therefore be written OF_2.

Several years later, a second compound of fluorine and oxygen was discovered: a brownish gas that proved to be made up of molecules containing two atoms of fluorine and two of oxygen. This is generally termed "fluorine dioxide" (F_2O_2) but the compound might better be termed *dioxygen fluoride* and the formula written O_2F_2.

In the case of O_2F_2, fluorine atoms are withdrawing electrons from an oxygen molecule. Since the ionization potential of the oxygen molecules is higher than that of radon and about as high as that of xenon, and since the oxygen molecule is not gaining in stability by the loss of those electrons, it follows that fluorine might be able to withdraw electrons from radon and xenon, too. In that case, one might well expect the formation of compounds between fluorine, on the one hand, and radon and xenon, on the other.

In OF_2, fluorine atoms are withdrawing electrons from a single oxygen atom. Since the oxygen atom has an ionization potential nearly as high as that of krypton, it might even be that compounds of krypton and fluorine were possible.

Thoughts such as these may have passed through the mind of Pauling in 1933. He took into account several other properties of the atoms concerned and finally concluded that, in his judgment, fluorine compounds of the heavier noble gases were indeed possible. He even felt that compounds with oxygen were also possible. (A German chemist, A. von Antropoff, had made a similar prediction in 1924, but his prediction was not based on the specific, valid reasoning that Pauling's was.)

This prediction having been made, two chemists at the California Institute of Technology (Pauling's school) undertook to test the matter and attempt to form a noble-gas compound. They were Don Merlin Lee Yost (b. 1893) and one of his graduate students, Albert L. Kaye.

It was not an easy task they had set themselves. Xenon was available only in small quantities and Yost and Kaye had but a total of 100 cubic centimeters at ordinary pressure at their disposal (about enough to fill a cocktail glass). Fluorine was not obtainable at all and Yost and Kaye had to prepare their own supply under difficult conditions. Their homemade fluorine-generating apparatus worked creakily—and sometimes did not work at all.

They tried the experiment and failed. Or at least, the results were inconclusive. They formed no compounds, but they were unable to show that a compound might not be formed under more favorable conditions.

Other chemists did not follow up the matter. Xenon remained a rare and expensive gas, and fluorine remained a most dangerously poisonous one. The chances of success in such an experiment did not warrant the expense and danger to most chemists, who, after all, had many other important investigations to make.

The matter was almost forgotten, and chemists continued to say in their lectures and to write in their textbooks that the noble gases did not form any compounds at all. This was, of course, correct.

Undoubtedly, some chemists said and wrote that the noble gases "could not" form compounds. This was a misstatement, for that much had not been proved. Indeed, from the arguments of Pauling, there seemed every reason to think they could indeed form compounds.

Uranium Hexafluoride

The situation might have remained at this stage for an indefinite period, were it not that interest in fluorine suddenly increased during World War II.

At that time, the American government was striving mightily to construct an atomic bomb. For that purpose, it was necessary to separate the isotope uranium-235 (which could be easily made to undergo fission and produce a vast explosion) from uranium-238 (which could not). However, the separation of the isotopes of a single element is usually a difficult task, and only 0.7 per cent of uranium metal consists of uranium-235. The problem was a formidable one.

One method of isotope separation takes advantage of the fact that a lighter molecule tends to move more rapidly than a heavier one. Suppose, for instance, that uranium were a gas made up of individual atoms. The uranium-235 atoms would be about 1.25 per cent lighter than the uranium-238 atoms and would move about 0.6 per cent faster.

This may not be much of a difference in speed, but it is enough. If this "uranium gas" were made to move through many narrow passages, the lighter isotope would gain a bit at each passage, and in the end could be obtained in nearly pure form. This is a *diffusion process*.

The only trouble was that uranium was not a gas, and that it became a gas only at 3,818° C. It simply was not practical to try to work with a gas that hot for the length of time that would be required to make the diffusion process work.

Of course, it is not necessary to work directly with uranium. One could work with a uranium compound. For instance, suppose uranium oxide (UO_3), the most common uranium compound, were a gas. Each oxygen atom has an atomic weight of 16, so that three of them weigh 48. A molecule of UO_3 containing a uranium-235 atom would have a molecular weight of $235 + 48$, or 283, while one with a uranium-238 atom would have a molecular weight of 286. The lighter molecule could have a lightness advantage of 1.05 per cent and would move about 0.5 per cent faster.

The trouble is that uranium oxide is not a gas; nor does it become a gas if it is heated. Instead, the molecule breaks up to form uranium dioxide (UO_2), which remains solid up to 2,500° C, and liquid for a good stretch above that.

In addition, not all oxygen atoms have an atomic weight of 16. Some have atomic weights of 17 or 18. If a molecule of UO_3, containing uranium-235, happens also to contain two oxygen-18 atoms and one oxygen-16 atom, it would be heavier than another molecule made up of a uranium-238 atom and three oxygen-16 atoms. This would tend to confuse matters in the diffusion process, even if an elevated temperature could be maintained and UO_3 were a gas.

What was needed, then, in the first place, was a uranium compound that was gaseous, or that could be made gaseous at a low temperature. But what compound, if any, would that be?

One difficulty was that hardly anything was known about the chemistry of uranium, even as late as 1940, for prior to the furor over the possibility of an atomic bomb, uranium had had practically no uses and chemists had paid almost no attention to it. They were not even sure of its melting point.

Eventually, however, fluorine was considered. When fluorine attacks atoms of other elements, molecules are sometimes formed in which an atom of the element attacked is surrounded on all sides by four or even six fluorine atoms. A molecule is then formed with its outer reaches entirely fluorine. It then seems to resemble fluorine in many ways.

Thus, separate fluorine molecules have little attraction for each other and are low boiling. In the same way, the higher fluorides of many metals form molecules that have little attraction for each other and are low boiling (though not so low boiling as fluorine itself, of course). Elements that are not gases in themselves and do not form gaseous oxides can become gases in the form of fluorides.

This is the explanation for the action of hydrogen fluoride on glass (a substance rich in the element *silicon*, which, in glass, is bound, for the most part, to oxygen atoms). Silicon is a very common element; indeed, next to oxygen, it is the most common element in the earth's crust. It is a solid with a melting point at 1,410° C and a boiling point at 2,355° C. The most common silicon compound is silicon dioxide (SiO_2), which has a melting point and boiling point in the same range as silicon itself.*

---

* Crystals of silicon dioxide are called quartz; ordinary sand is composed of fragments of impure silicon dioxide crystals.

In the presence of hydrogen fluoride, the silicon atoms in glass will be pulled away from the oxygen atoms that hold them. They combine with four fluorine atoms instead, to form silicon tetrafluoride (SiF_4); that is a gas, with a boiling point of $-86°$ C. The silicon tetrafluoride leaves the glass, what is left crumbles, and the glass is etched.

Could not the same situation apply to uranium? Actually, it does. If uranium dioxide is treated with hydrogen fluoride, uranium tetrafluoride (UF_4) is formed. Since the uranium atom is too large to be satisfactorily surrounded by four fluorine atoms and there is considerable attraction between such molecules, UF_4 remains solid up to high temperatures. However, if UF_4 is subjected to the action of fluorine itself, each uranium atom picks up two more fluorine atoms and *uranium hexafluoride* (UF_6) is formed.

The uranium atom is now surrounded by fluorine atoms. Uranium hexafluoride is a white solid at room temperature, but if it is heated to a temperature of $56°$ C it is converted directly into a vapor without first melting. It is easy to maintain a temperature of $56°$ C for indefinite periods and to work with gaseous UF_6. UF_6 is the only uranium compound known to be gaseous at so low a temperature.

Furthermore, only one kind of fluorine isotope occurs in nature, fluorine-19, so that the situation is not confused by fluorine atoms of different weights. Each fluorine atom has an atomic weight of 19 and six such fluorine atoms have an atomic weight of 114. A molecule of UF_6 containing uranium-235 has a molecular weight of 349, and each molecule containing uranium-238 has one of 352. The molecule containing uranium-235 is 0.85 per cent lighter and moves 0.4 per cent faster than the molecule containing uranium-238.

This is cutting matters pretty fine, but it could be made to work and it *was* made to work. Uranium-235 was extracted from uranium and the atomic bomb came into existence in 1945.

The intense interest in fluorine that arose out of the necessity of preparing uranium hexafluoride brought about the development of techniques for the safe storage and handling of fluorine. Through the 1950's, fluorine continued to attract further attention as a possible substitute for liquid oxygen in rocketry. Combinations of liquid hydrogen and liquid fluorine would give the most powerful thrusts possible in ordinary chemical rockets. Fluorine can now be handled in quantity, and experimenters no longer have to suffer the difficulties that brought the efforts of Yost and Kaye to naught.

10

Noble-Gas Compounds

Platinum Hexafluoride

The glamorous success of uranium hexafluoride caused some chemists to grow interested in highly fluorinated compounds generally, and in those of the platinum family of metals* in particular. The platinum metals, like uranium, are high melting and high boiling, and do not generally form compounds that are gases at easily reached temperatures.

At Argonne National Laboratory, the hexafluorides of several of the platinum metals were prepared and were found to be easily converted to the gaseous state. *Osmium hexafluoride* (OsF_6), for instance, is a green solid that melts at 32° C (the

---

* These include the six metals: platinum, osmium, iridium, palladium, ruthenium, and rhodium.

temperature of a summer afternoon) and boils at 46° C. *Platinum hexafluoride* (PtF_6), a deep red solid, requires temperatures a bit higher than that (it does not melt until 57.6° C) but it can be converted into a deep red vapor without much trouble.

Among the chemists who became interested in these compounds was Neil Bartlett at the University of British Columbia. In the early 1960's, he was working, not only with platinum hexafluoride, but also with *ruthenium hexafluoride* (RuF_6) and *rhodium hexafluoride* (RhF_6). These highly fluorinated compounds turned out to be surprisingly active. Of the three with which Bartlett was working, platinum hexafluoride was most active, and he studied its reactions with particular interest.

Rather to his surprise, he found that platinum hexafluoride reacted with oxygen to form dioxygen platinofluoride (O_2PtF_6). The situation was similar to that in which oxygen reacted with fluorine itself to form dioxygen fluoride (O_2F_2).

The ionization potential of an oxygen molecule, Bartlett knew, is about that of xenon. That a molecule such as O_2F_2 could exist was one of the reasons for supposing that fluorine might also be able to combine with xenon. Yost and Kaye had tried to accomplish this, but had failed. By the same token, the fact that O_2PtF_6 could exist made it reasonable to suppose that platinum hexafluoride might react with xenon.

Bartlett therefore prepared to make another attempt (the first since that of Yost and Kaye twenty-nine years before) to form a xenon compound. Bartlett had an important advantage in that he could work with platinum hexafluoride, easier to get and to handle than fluorine had been in Yost's day.

In 1962, Bartlett set up an apparatus containing platinum hexafluoride vapors and xenon, separated by a thin glass partition. When the partition was broken, the two gases mixed and a yellow powder formed. Bartlett felt he must have formed xenon platinofluoride ($XePtF_6$).

He then went on to react xenon with rhodium hexafluoride,

which is almost as active as platinum hexafluoride. He prepared what seemed to be xenon rhodiofluoride ($XeRhF_6$), a deep red substance. He was unable, however, to prepare compounds of krypton, which have a higher ionization potential than xenon. Undoubtedly, had radon been available, he would have been able to form the platinofluoride and rhodiofluoride of radon.

Xenon and Fluorine

Bartlett's findings were reported in a British chemical journal in June 1962, and astounded the chemical world. In particular, the chemists at Argonne National Laboratory, where the various hexafluorides of the platinum metals had first been studied in detail, were fascinated. They at once set about confirming Bartlett's report.

They did this successfully, and, indeed, went on to react xenon with ruthenium hexafluoride to form what seemed xenon rutheniofluoride ($XeRuF_6$). The chemists, Howard H. Claasen, Henry Selig, and John G. Malm, were not entirely satisfied to leave things at that. The compounds being formed were not quite satisfactory.

Suppose, for instance, that in reacting xenon with ruthenium hexafluoride, one really did form $XeRuF_6$. In that case, for every atom of xenon tied up in such a compound, one molecule of RuF_6 should also be tied up. However, this was not so. Instead, analysis showed that as many as three molecules of RuF_6 were tied up for every atom of xenon.

This could mean that a compound such as $XeRuF_6$ was formed, with three molecules of RuF_6 hanging on to each atom of xenon. Or else, it could mean that various molecules of RuF_6 were giving up single atoms of fluorine, which were in turn attaching themselves to xenon. Suppose that three molecules of RuF_6 lost a fluorine atom apiece in this way for each atom of xenon tied up. That would account for the results, too, and in that case what was really being formed was a compound of xenon with fluorine and not with RuF_6.

There was, however, no point in speculating too deeply on the matter. If a compound of xenon and fluorine could be formed and was being formed, the best course of procedure was to check the matter by mixing xenon and fluorine under the most favorable conditions and to see what happened then.

On August 2, 1962, the Argonne chemists proceeded to run an experiment very similar to that of Yost and Kaye. They had much more elaborate and effective methods for handling fluorine, however, and they had ample supplies of both it and xenon.

Since it seemed quite clear from the number of RuF_6 molecules consumed (and from Pauling's early theoretical predictions) that each xenon atom would be attached to several fluorine atoms, the mixture was weighted heavily in favor of fluorine. The mixture consisted of five molecules of fluorine (containing ten fluorine atoms) for every xenon atom. If xenon reacted with fluorine, the absolute maximum number of fluorine atoms each xenon atom could hang on to was eight, so that they were bound to end up with fluorine left over.

They placed the mixture in a nickel can with a 90-cubic centimeter capacity and heated it for one hour at 400° C. They hoped that some of the xenon had reacted by then, and were anxious to find out if that were so without opening the can. If it were not so, they could try heating at higher temperatures or for longer intervals.

What they did, then, was to cool the can rapidly to − 195° C. At that temperature, fluorine becomes a liquid, but one that still gives off a considerable quantity of vapor. Xenon, on the other hand, is frozen solid at so low a temperature.

The nickel can was then attached to a vacuum pump and the vapors from within were withdrawn. It was expected that all the fluorine would be removed and all the xenon left behind. Any compound formed would surely be even higher-melting than xenon, so it would remain behind, too.

Once the vapors were removed and only xenon (and possibly some xenon compound) was left, the can was sealed again and slowly allowed to warm up. The xenon would gradually turn into a gas while any compound, it was hoped, would remain solid.

They knew exactly how much xenon was present to begin with. If the xenon pressure turned out to be that value, then no compound had been formed. If the pressure dropped, then one could hope that a compound had been formed. The greater the pressure drop, the more compound had been formed.

To their delight, virtually no xenon pressure showed up at all. Apparently, all the xenon had formed a compound with fluorine after one hour at 400° C. It was as easy as that. They repeated the experiment a number of times, and obtained the compound, which turned out to be a reasonably stable solid at room temperature. They even heated it gently to a vapor which solidified again on a cold surface, forming beautiful transparent crystals.

It was simple to analyze the compound and to show that its molecule was made up of one atom of xenon and four of fluorine. The Argonne chemists had formed *xenon tetrafluoride*, XeF_4.

This accomplishment was quickly announced. If there had been excitement among chemists before, there was sheer pandemonium now. Chemists everywhere began to throw themselves into work on noble-gas compounds.

Soon, at Argonne and elsewhere, two other fluorides of xenon were prepared. When a mixture of xenon and fluorine was exposed to the action of ultraviolet light, *xenon difluoride* (XeF_2) was formed. When xenon was mixed with a particularly large quantity of fluorine (one atom of xenon to twenty molecules of fluorine), then *xenon hexafluoride* (XeF_6) was formed.

All three fluorides form colorless crystals that remain quite stable at room temperature. They are so stable, in fact, that, if carefully heated, their melting points can be established. The greater the quantity of fluorine in the molecule, the lower the melting point: that of XeF_2 is 140° C, that of XeF_4, about 114° C, and that of XeF_6 is 46° C. XeF_2 dissolves easily in water and decomposes gradually to xenon and fluorine, the fluorine reacting with the water at once to form oxygen and HF.

The xenon fluorides give off vapor easily even while still solid. Both XeF_2 and XeF_4 yield colorless vapors, but that of XeF_6 is pale yellow-green, rather like the color of fluorine itself. The odor of XeF_2 vapor is penetrating and nauseating.

The hold of fluorine on the xenon atom is somewhat precarious, however, and the xenon fluoride molecules are easily broken up. Thus, if any of the fluorides are mixed with hydrogen, the fluorine atoms add on to hydrogen atoms to form hydrogen fluoride, and gaseous xenon is left behind.

Attempts were made to produce compounds of other noble gases. Despite the difficulty of working with radon, some results were obtained at Argonne. Tiny quantities of radon were heated with fluorine and a radon fluoride seems definitely to have been formed, though exactly which fluoride is not certain. Radon fluoride, as is to be expected, gave indications of being more stable than the xenon fluorides.

Since radon has a lower ionization potential than xenon, it was felt that elements less electronegative than fluorine might form compounds with it. However, no reaction was observed between radon and either oxygen or chlorine (the second and third most electronegative element).

Krypton presented the reverse problem. It could be obtained in reasonable quantities, being more common than xenon, but the ionization potential of krypton was higher than that of xenon, so that krypton compounds might be expected to be formed with greater difficulty and to be less stable once formed. This turned out to be so.

In fact, when krypton and fluorine are heated together in a nickel container in the same proportions and under the same conditions that sufficed for xenon, nothing happened; no krypton compound was formed. Nor did krypton and fluorine react under exposure to ultraviolet.

However, when chemists at Temple University in Philadelphia passed electric sparks through a mixture of krypton and fluorine, they brought about the formation of *krypton tetrafluoride* (KrF_4). Later, *krypton difluoride* (KrF_2) was formed at the University of California when electric discharges were sent through mixtures of krypton and fluorine at liquid-nitrogen temperatures.

Krypton tetrafluoride forms beautiful, transparent crystals, just as xenon tetrafluoride does, but krypton tetrafluoride is much less stable. In order to keep the krypton tetrafluoride from breaking down to krypton and fluorine, it must be stored at temperatures well below zero.

Argon, neon, and helium have successively higher ionization potentials than krypton; nothing yet has succeeded in forcing them into combination with any substance—not even with fluorine.

Looking at matters overall, we see that of the six noble gases, helium, neon, and argon still form no compounds as far as we now know; krypton forms a few uncomfortably unstable ones; and radon can be the source of only extremely tiny quantities of compounds.

By all odds then, xenon remains the gas to concentrate on as far as the noble-gas compounds are concerned. Only xenon compounds are likely ever to be formed in reasonable quantities and with reasonable stabilities.

Xenon and Oxygen

Although xenon does not react with oxygen directly, it was found possible to form compounds of xenon and oxygen indirectly by beginning with the xenon fluorides, rather than with xenon itself.

It seemed logical to test whether xenon hexafluoride, like hydrogen fluoride, might not react with silicon dioxide (SiO_2). A small quantity of XeF_6 was placed in a quartz flask (quartz being silicon dioxide) and heated to the point where the XeF_6 was present as the yellow-green vapor. Sure enough, the inner surface of the flask slowly etched in the course of the next couple of days while the yellow-green color disappeared.

Apparently, two molecules of xenon hexafluoride each contributed two fluorine atoms, which replaced the oxygen atoms in the silicon dioxide to form silicon tetrafluoride. The oxygen atoms given up by the silicon dioxide entered the xenon compound instead, each oxygen atom substituting for two fluorine atoms. All this can be represented in a chemical equation as follows:

$$2\ XeF_6 + SiO_2 \longrightarrow 2\ XeOF_4 + SiF_4$$

The new compound, $XeOF_4$, is *xenon oxytetrafluoride* and was the first oxygen-containing noble-gas compound to be discovered.

If xenon oxytetrafluoride is allowed to react further with additional silicon dioxide, more fluorine atoms are given up to silicon, and additional oxygen atoms are accepted in its place, until finally a compound of xenon and oxygen only is formed. This is *xenon trioxide* (XeO_3).

The xenon fluorides also react with water (H_2O). The fluorine atoms seize hydrogen atoms to form hydrogen fluoride. The fate of the xenon and oxygen differs with the particular xenon fluoride used.

If xenon difluoride (XeF_2) reacts with water, the xenon and oxygen are both liberated as separate gases. If xenon hexafluoride (XeF_6) reacts with water, the xenon and oxygen combine to form xenon trioxide (XeO_3). If xenon tetrafluoride (XeF_4) reacts with water, a little of both happens; xenon trioxide, xenon, and oxygen are all formed.

Xenon oxytetrafluoride differs from the xenon fluorides in

having a much lower melting point, $-28°$ C. At room temperature, it is a clear, colorless liquid, giving off vapors easily.

Xenon trioxide, on the other hand, is dangerous. Oxygen, being less electronegative than fluorine, forms a compound with xenon with greater difficulty and hangs on to the xenon atom more precariously. Oxygen is much more ready to let go, so to speak, than fluorine is; when oxygen does let go, it will do so all at once and xenon trioxide will then explode. It will explode on gentle heating, or when rubbed, or even, sometimes, for no visible reason. On exploding, it forms the two gases, xenon and oxygen, and therefore leaves no residue at all; it is simply gone.

To make matters worse, if xenon tetrafluoride or xenon hexafluoride (themselves quite safe) is allowed to grow damp, some xenon trioxide may form and, eventually, explode. In the first months of research into the noble-gas compounds, there were some explosions of this sort; none of them, fortunately, serious. Chemists learned to keep their xenon fluorides as dry as possible when they were stored, and after that there was no further trouble.

Xenon trioxide dissolves easily in water and, when in solution, is quite safe. It can be considered as combining with a molecule of water in solution to form H_2XeO_4, a compound called *xenic acid*.

If xenon hexafluoride is dissolved in water containing sodium hydroxide under appropriate conditions, a compound is formed that is called *sodium perxenate* (Na_4XeO_6). Compounds in which atoms of metals other than sodium are involved can also be formed. These are all white solids which are stable at room temperature.

Other xenon compounds remain possible and may yet be prepared. Some chemists, for instance, maintain that additional oxides and fluorides, such as XeO_2 and XeF, ought to be possible. Even the possibility of XeN_2 (xenon nitride) is suggested. If the last compound were produced, it would be the first known compound of a noble gas with nitrogen.

The Uses of the Noble-Gas Compounds

Now that we have noble-gas compounds, what good are they?

Actually, at the very best, their uses will always be limited, for nothing we can do will make xenon anything other than a rare substance. That means that the xenon compounds, no matter how we improve the techniques of preparation, will remain rare and expensive. They will never be used on a really large scale.

But there are small-scale uses that can be valuable. For instance, xenon is hard to store in concentrated form, as an element. It is a gas, and, under ordinary conditions, a liter of it weighs only about 6 grams (about ¼ ounce). To squeeze more xenon into that liter, one might cool it into liquid form. A liter of liquid xenon weighs about 3,500 grams (nearly 8 pounds). Keeping xenon liquid is a chore, however, for it must be maintained at less than $-107°$ C.

To have xenon that concentrated at ordinary temperatures, one must place it under pressure. A pressure equal to nearly 600 times that of the atmosphere would squeeze 3,500 grams of gaseous xenon into one liter. But compressing the gas is a chore, too, and both liquefied gases and compressed gases have their dangers.

Suppose, though, that you do not try to store xenon as such at all, but form xenon difluoride, and store that. The density of xenon difluoride is about 4.3 grams per cubic centimeter. A liter of well-packed crystals of that compound would weigh about 4,000 grams. Since 78 per cent of the weight of xenon difluoride is xenon, that liter of xenon difluoride ought to contain about 3,000 grams of xenon. As xenon difluoride, in other words, xenon can be stored almost as compactly as though it had been liquefied; yet neither low temperatures nor high pressures would be required.

By similar reasoning, the xenon fluorides represent a handy

way of storing fluorine in considerable concentration. A liter of
xenon hexafluoride could contain up to 1,300 grams of fluorine
as compared with 1,700 grams in a liter of liquid fluorine. As
xenon hexafluoride, fluorine would be stored in compact form
without the use of either low temperatures or high pressures;
and xenon hexafluoride is much safer than liquid fluorine would
be.

Furthermore, xenon and fluorine are both readily on tap
when stored as xenon fluorides. The xenon fluorides are easily
broken down to yield a flood of elementary fluorine that will
then react with other substances present, so that the xenon
fluorides will be able to act as useful *fluoridation agents* to carry
through specialized reactions. And, of course, xenon will be left
behind, either to be used for its own specialized purposes, or to
be made available for combination with further supplies of
fluorine.

The general usefulness of fluoridation agents has increased
since World War II. In the course of the increased interest in
fluorine during atomic bomb work, it was desired, for instance,
to produce greases that could withstand the action of fluorine.
No ordinary greases could.

Many greases are organic compounds—that is, compounds
built up of molecules containing long chains or rings of carbon
atoms.* In ordinary organic compounds, the carbon atoms are
attached mainly to hydrogen atoms, with other atoms (oxygen
and nitrogen in particular) added here and there. Organic compounds are thus primarily *hydrocarbon* in nature.

In the early 1940's, however, it was found that fluorine atoms
could replace hydrogen atoms wherever they occurred in the
hydrocarbon chains and rings. In that way, a whole series of
fluorocarbons could be formed. Fluorocarbon greases were just

---

* The important compounds of living tissue are composed of such
molecules; hence the name "organic."

what was needed, for since fluorine had already added on to the molecule at every possible point, the substance was immune to further attack.

In addition, fluorine held on more tightly to the carbon atom than hydrogen, so that fluorocarbons do not take part in chemical reactions as readily as hydrocarbons. They are more resistant to heat, do not burn, are unaffected by water or by liquids that dissolve ordinary organic substances. They are not toxic; they are waterproof; they do not conduct an electric current. Plastics built up out of fluorocarbons are more inert than those built up out of hydrocarbons. For example, frying pans are coated with fluorocarbon plastic, which is not decomposed even at frying heat. Such frying pans can be used without fat, for food will not stick to the inert fluorocarbon.

Chemists are just scratching the surface of what may prove an extremely intricate world of fluorocarbon compounds, and of fluorohydrocarbon compounds, too. It may prove that some of them will be more easily formed by treatment with xenon fluorides than in any other way, and this alone might allow the noble-gas compounds to "pay their way."

Xenon fluoride has an additional advantage over most other fluorides in that once the fluorine is used in some reaction, no precautions are necessary, since there is nothing left over that requires getting rid of. The xenon that remains is a gas that reenters the atmosphere from which it came in the first place. It is nontoxic, nonflammable, nonexplosive, nonodorous—in short, utterly harmless. In high concentrations, it is an anesthetic, but such concentrations are not likely to be met with in ordinary work with the xenon fluorides.

Xenon trioxide and the perxenates are among the most active compounds known. They hang together by the skin of their teeth, so to speak, and in the presence of other substances easily fall apart, leaving the oxygen atom to combine with other substances. These xenon/oxygen compounds are therefore among the strongest *oxidizing agents* known.

Xenon trioxide (which might conceivably come to be used as a specialized small-scale explosive) has actually been used, for instance, to bring about chemical changes involving the element plutonium. Plutonium is a man-made element that does not occur in nature except in the barest traces, but it is useful in connection with nuclear power.

Work with plutonium is bound to be fairly small scale for the most part so that it could be profitable to use xenon trioxide to bring about plutonium reactions, particularly when it turns out that the residue left behind after the xenon trioxide is consumed is merely water and xenon. There is no contamination problem.

No doubt other uses will be uncovered.

A *Final Word*

The greatest service of the noble-gas compounds has, however, been an imponderable one.

Scientists sometimes have a tendency to be complacent. They tend to think that many things are "known" and "settled" and sometimes are too ready to make flat statements.

Undoubtedly, some chemists did not say, as they should have: "As far as we know, the noble gases do not form compounds," but said instead (as they should not have): "The noble gases cannot form compounds under any conditions."

For this reason, the discovery of the noble-gas compounds came as a shock to some chemists and as a healthy object lesson to all. The universe is a very complicated place and there is very little of it we have penetrated. Even those portions of the universe with which we feel well acquainted can still hold surprises.

The scientist must never sit back too comfortably; he must never let himself get off guard. It will be a long while, we can hope, before he forgets the lesson of the noble-gas compounds in this respect.

And yet, let us not go to the other extreme, either, of thinking that chemists have fallen down on their job more than they actually have. Some people who are not themselves scientists have watched the events of the last few years with great glee. That is understandable. It is always funny when a dignified, pompous man suddenly has an accident that destroys his dignity. It is only human to laugh. When the "know-it-all" scientists suddenly find themselves caught by surprise, they can expect to be laughed at.

Nevertheless, we must know what we are laughing at. It is not really true, as some critics have said, that scientists, as a group, are authoritarian; that they make pronouncements that must be accepted as gospel truth; that they have such faith in old theories that they forget to question them any longer.

The history of the noble gases is not evidence that all this is so; rather it is evidence that all this is *not* so.

Many chemists may have accepted the fact that noble gases do not form compounds, but many others were fully aware that they might. Indeed, the history of twentieth-century chemistry contains a number of examples of chemists trying to form noble-gas compounds of one sort or another.

It might seem to some (and I have heard it said) that all any chemist would have had to do to disprove the complete inertness of the noble gases was to have mixed xenon and fluorine in a nickel pot and that anyone could have done this at any time over the past sixty years. The only reason this was not done, the critics go on to say, was that chemists were so sure it would not work, that they could not be bothered to try.

All this is sheer rot. There are two basic reasons why chemists did not experiment with xenon and fluorine and neither involved anything as silly as "knowing in advance it would not work."

First, scientists have many interests* and very few chemists prior to the 1960's happened to be interested in the chemistry of fluorine or of the noble gases. As an example, my own field of research in the 1950's was the nucleic acids. It is not conceivable that I would ever have dreamed of working with xenon and fluorine, regardless of my feelings about the possibility of their forming a compound.

Second, even if a chemist had wished to test the matter of xenon and fluorine, he would have faced insuperable handicaps. Xenon was rare and hard to obtain. Fluorine was dangerous and hard to obtain. Prior to World War II, any chemist who tried to mix xenon and fluorine would have probably ended with inconclusive results, as Yost and Kaye did because of the primitiveness of their equipment—or, if he were not careful, he might have ended dead.

It was only in the course of the 1940's that chemists learned to deal with fluorine with safety. Special equipment had to be used and special experience had to be gained.

Even by the 1950's, there were only a few places in the world where xenon and fluorine could have been experimented with profitably. Chemists then began working on many worthwhile aspects of fluorine chemistry and technology, and, *in due course,* reached the problem of the noble-gas compounds.

The crucial reaction between xenon and fluorine might have been conducted successfully ten years sooner than it was, but (except through a stroke of amazing luck) no earlier. Under the circumstances, a ten-year delay is not unreasonable.

Another thing that is sometimes said is that the formation of the noble-gas compounds completely smashed chemical the-

---

* It must never be forgotten that the number of scientists is finite and the number of scientific problems is infinite.

ories of valence and overturned the chemist's notion of the manner in which atoms are held together in molecules, leaving him in a state of foolish confusion.

Precisely the opposite is the case!

The noble-gas compounds would have upset the simple theories of valence developed a hundred years ago in the time of Mendeléev (see Page 29) when practically nothing was known about the structure of molecules, and nothing at all was known about the internal structure of the atom.

By the early 1930's, however, Pauling and others had worked out in detail new and better theories of valence—theories that took into account the existence of electrons. It was by using these new theories of valence that Pauling was able to predict the possible existence of xenon fluorides.

When xenon fluorides were formed, they did not upset chemical theories of valence; they *confirmed* them. Indeed, if it had been found that xenon fluorides could *not* be formed, it would be *then* that chemists would have been puzzled and would have had to start scratching their heads and wondering what was wrong.

Once the xenon compounds were formed, chemists had a perfect opportunity to study their structures with all the new devices developed in the last couple of decades, in order to see how those structures fit in with modern electronic theories of valence.

So far, the structure of the noble-gas compounds fits modern theories of valence at every point!

Still, the coming of the noble-gas compounds was an astonishing and refreshing development; many chemists, whose field lay elsewhere and who were not familiar with Pauling's theoretical work, were surprised.

And that is good, for we can turn to the future with uplifted hearts. Surprises will always exist everywhere. Science is not always a severe and sour task mistress, but has her moments of gayety and skittishness—and who can complain about that?

Even the noble gases, themselves, which have already offered us so many surprises in the course of the history of chemistry, may not be finished with us yet.

We need only wait and see.

SOME NOTABLE DATES IN NOBLE-GAS HISTORY

1529   Agricola describes fluorspar.

1640   Van Helmont invents word "gas."

1665   Newton produces light spectrum.

1670   Schwanhard discovers glass-etching vapors from acidified fluorspar.

1727   Hales separates gases over water.

1756   Black discovers carbon dioxide in air.

1766   Cavendish discovers hydrogen.

1771   Scheele studies "fluoric acid."

1772   Rutherford discovers nitrogen.

1774   Priestley discovers oxygen.

1775   Lavoisier suggests air to be a mixture of oxygen and nitrogen.

1783   Montgolfier brothers construct the first balloon.

1785   Cavendish isolates inert constituent of atmosphere (argon).

1803   Dalton advances atomic theory.

1807   Davy isolates potassium and sodium.

1810   Davy shows chlorine to be an element.

1813   Davy shows "fluoric acid" to be made up of hydrogen and fluorine.

1814   Fraunhofer studies spectral lines.

1815   Prout's hypothesis published.

1828   Berzelius "disproves" Prout's hypothesis.

1848   Kelvin proposes absolute temperature scale.

1859   Kirchhoff and Bunsen invent spectroscope.

1860   Kirchhoff and Bunsen discover cesium spectroscopically.

1861   Ångström discovers hydrogen in the sun spectroscopically.

1868   Janssen and Lockyer observe new spectral line (helium) in the sun.

1869   Mendeléev works out the periodic table of the elements.

1877   Cailletet liquefies oxygen and nitrogen.

1886   Moissan isolates fluorine.

1890   Hillebrand identifies occluded gas (helium) as nitrogen.

1892   Rayleigh publishes his problem concerning the density of nitrogen.

1894   Rayleigh and Ramsay discover argon.

1895   Ramsay discovers helium on earth; Linde produces liquid air in quantity.

1896   Becquerel discovers radioactivity.

1898   Ramsay and Travers discover krypton, neon, and xenon; the Curies discover polonium and radium; Dewar liquefies hydrogen.

1900   Dorn discovers radon; Zeppelin invents dirigible.

1901   Invention of the vapor lamp.

1904   Ramsay receives Nobel Prize in chemistry; Rayleigh receives Nobel Prize in physics.

1906   Moissan receives Nobel Prize in chemistry; Campbell discovers radioactivity of potassium.

1908   Kamerlingh-Onnes liquefies helium.

1909   Rutherford shows alpha particles to be helium nuclei; advances theory of nuclear atom.

1910   Ramsay shows radon to be noble gas.

1911   Kamerlingh-Onnes discovers superconductivity; Soddy advances theory of isotopes.

1912   Thomson demonstrates existence of neon isotopes.

1913   Moseley works out system of atomic numbers; Kamerlingh-Onnes receives Nobel Prize in physics.

1914   Langmuir introduces use of argon in light bulbs; Franck and Hertz work out method of determining ionization potentials.

1919   Aston invents the mass spectrograph.

1926   Helium is solidified.

1927   Claude invents "neon lights"; oxygen difluoride formed.

1929   Shielded arc-welding with argon introduced.

1932   Pauling prepares electronegativity list of elements.

1933   Pauling predicts existence of xenon fluorides; Yost and Kaye fail in effort to prepare xenon fluorides; superconductive substances found to be perfectly diamagnetic.

1935   Helium II discovered.
1945   First atomic bomb exploded.
1956   Cryotron invented (used at liquid helium temperatures).
1957   Spark chamber invented (helium and neon used).
1960   Continuous neon-helium gas laser invented.
1962   Noble-gas compounds first prepared.

Index

absolute scale, 102
absolute zero, 102
actinium emanation, 45
actinon, 45, 51
Agricola, George, 131
air, 2; density of, 92–93; dephlogisticated, 6; liquid, 38; phlogisticated, 6
alkali metals, 65, 123
alkaline earth metals, 63
alpha particles, 72
aluminum, 84, 109
Alvarez, Luis W., 75
ammonia, 20, 37, 93, 97
Ampère, André M., 133
anesthesia, 90
Ångström, Anders J., 13
Antropoff, A. von, 139
arc-welding, 84
argon, 26, 151; abundance of, 68, 76–77, 80; atom of, 31; atomic number of, 50; atomic weight of, 32; boiling point of, 39, 104; density of, 31, 93; electron distribution in, 62, 66; ionization potential of, 125; isotopes of, 54, 56–57; light bulbs and, 83; melting-point of, 106; nuclear structure of, 58; periodic table and, 33–35; solubility of, 99; symbol

of, 52 n.; uses of, 83–85; valence of, 30; welding and, 84–85
argon-36, 74
argon-37, 55
argon-38, 74, 80–81
argon-39, 55, 88
argon-40, 57; formation of, 74–76
argon-41, 89
argon glow lamp, 87
argon hydrate, 115
arsenic, 136
astatine, 50, 65
Aston, Francis W., 53
atmosphere, 70–71; composition of, 7, 9–11, 26, 41–42
atom(s), 17; neutral, 52; nuclear, 48
atomic bombs, 78, 140
atomic hydrogen torch, 84
atomic number, 49
atomic theory, 16–17
atomic weight, 17; atomic number and, 49–50
azote, 7

balloons, 92
barium, 63, 134
Bartlett, Neil, 146
Becquerel, Antoine H., 43
"bends," 98

165

beryllium, 63
Berzelius, Jöns J., 18
beta particles, 75
Black, Joseph, 5
boiling point, 100
bromine, 65, 129
Bunsen, Robert W. von, 12

Cailletet, Louis P., 38
caisson disease, 98
calcium, 63, 134
calcium-40, 76
calcium fluoride, 135
Campbell, Norman R., 74
cancer, 90
carbon, 48, 82, 101; abundance of, 68; valence of, 118
carbon dioxide, 3, 5, 93, 98
carbon monoxide, 93, 98, 103, 106
Cavendish, Henry, 7, 9–10, 25, 93, 113
cesium, 13, 65, 123
Chadwick, James, 57
Charles, Jacques A. C., 93
chlorine, 133; density of, 93; electron distribution of, 65; electronegativity of, 129; liquefaction of, 37
Claasen, Howard H., 147
clathrate compound, 116
Claude, Georges, 86
cleveite, 36
cobalt, 47
copper, 107, 109, 137
cosmic-ray particles, 73
Crookes, William, 13, 36
cryogenics, 105
cryotron, 111
Curie, Marie S., 43–44
Curie, Pierre, 44

Dalton, John, 16
Davy, Humphry, 133–134
decomposition, 100 n.

Dewar, James, 103
diamagnetism, 109
diffusion process, 141
dioxygen fluoride, 139
dioxygen platinofluoride, 146
dirigibles, 93
distillation, fractional, 38
Dorn, Friedrich E., 45

Edison, Thomas A., 82
electron(s), 48; transfer of, 118 ff.
electron shells, 61–66
electronegativity, 129
elements, 2; abundance of, 67–68; daughter, 43; families of, 63–66; periodic table of, 29; radioactive, 43; stable, 51; valence of, 29–30
emanon, 45
escape velocity, 69

film flow, 108
fission, 78
fission products, 79
fluores, 131
fluorescence, 132 n.
fluorescent lights, 87
fluoric acid, 132
fluoridation agents, 155
fluorine, 59, 130 ff.; boiling point of, 103; compounds of, 142–143; electron distribution of, 65; electronegativity of, 129; isolation of, 133–137; isotopes of, 143; melting point of, 106; name of, 133; oxygen and, 137–139; rocketry and, 144; xenon and, 147–150
fluorine dioxide, 138
fluorine monoxide, 138
fluorite, 132
fluorocarbons, 155
fluorspar, 132
francium, 50, 65, 123
Franck, James, 119
Fraunhofer, Joseph von, 12

Fraunhofer lines, 12
Frémy Edmond, 135

gas(es), 3, 6; density of, 92 ff.; diatomic, 31; isolation of, 4; liquefaction of, 37–38; monatomic, 31; natural, 72; occluded, 15; permanent, 38; solubilities of, 97–99
gas lasers, 88
germanium, 85
glass, 143
gold, 109, 118

Hales, Stephen, 4, 8
halogens, 64, 128–129
helium, 14, 36, 76, 151; abundance of, 67–68, 72–74, 77, 80; atmosphere and, 73; atomic number of, 50; atomic weight of, 36; balloons and, 94–95; boiling point of, 104; conservation of, 111; density of, 92–93; electron distribution of, 66; formation of, 72; ionization potential of, 125; isotopes of, 54; lifting power of, 94–95; liquefaction of, 105; liquid, 105; melting point of, 106; name of, 36 n.; nuclear structure of, 60; solid, 106; solubility of, 99; symbol of, 52 n.; uses of, 91 ff.; wells of, 72–73
helium-3, 93 n., 95, 108; abundance of, 80–81; boiling point of, 105 n.; formation of, 73–74
helium-4, 73
helium-6, 55
helium I, 107
helium II, 107
helium-oxygen atmospheres, 96–99
hemoglobin, 116
Hertz, Gustav, 119
Hillebrand, William F., 15, 35, 72
Hindenburg, 96
Huggins, William, 13
hydrocarbons, 155

hydrochloric acid, 133
hydrofluoric acid, 133
hydrogen, 4, 17; abundance of, 67–68; atomic weight of, 19; balloons, 93–94; boiling point of, 103; density of, 19, 92–93; discovery of, 7–8; earth's atmosphere and, 70–71; electron distribution of, 65; ionization potential of, 119–120; isotopes of, 59; lifting power of, 94–95; liquefaction of, 103; liquid, 112; melting point of, 106; nuclear structure of, 48, 59; solubility of, 98; sun and, 13; viscosity of, 107
hydrogen-2, 92 n.
hydrogen-3, 73
hydrogen chloride, 93, 97, 133
hydrogen fluoride, 133, 135
hydrogen molecules, 22
hydrogen sulfide, 93
hydroquinone, 116

indium, 13
iodine, 34, 65, 129
ion, positive, 52
ionization potential, 119
iridium, 109, 137, 145 n.
isotopes, 50 ff.; separation of, 140–143

Janssen, Pierre J. C., 14
Javan, Ali, 88
Jupiter, 69

Kammerlingh-Onnes, Heike, 105–106, 108
Kaye, Albert L., 139, 146, 159
K-capture, 75
Kelvin, Lord, 102
Kirchhoff, Gustav R., 12
krypton, 39; abundance of, 68, 77, 80; atomic number of, 50; boiling point of, 104; compounds of, 150–151; density of, 93; electron dis-

krypton (cont'd)
    tribution of, 66; formation of, 79;
    ionization potential of, 125; iso-
    topes of, 54; melting point of,
    106; nuclear structure of, 60; solu-
    bility of, 99; symbol of, 52 n.; uses
    of, 88–90
krypton-78, 80–81
krypton-79, 89
krypton-81, 55, 88
krypton-85, 89
krypton-87, 55
krypton difluoride, 151
krypton hydrate, 115
krypton tetrafluoride, 151
krypton vapor lamp, 90

Langmuir, Irving, 83
lanthanum, 109
laser, 87–88
Lavoisier, Antoine L., 6, 132–133
lead, 72, 76
light, 11
lighting, electrical, 82–83
Linde, Karl von, 38
liquid state, 100
lithium, 65, 123
Lockyer, Joseph N., 14, 36
Louyet, Paulin, 135

magnesium, 25, 134; electron dis-
    tribution in, 63; ionization poten-
    tial of, 121–122, 126
magnetic fields, 109–110
Maiman, Theodore H., 88
Malm, John G., 147
manganese, 118
Mars, 70
mass number, 53
mass spectrograph, 53
Mendeléev, Dmitri I., 29, 33, 50,
    117, 160
melting point, 100
mercuric oxide, 6

mercury, 101; superconductivity of,
    109
mercury vapor lamp, 85–86
meteorites, 76
methane, 93
Moissan, Ferdinand F. H., 136
molecules, 22
Montgolfier, Jacques É., 92
Montgolfier, Joseph M., 92
moon, 70, 79
Moseley, Henry Gwyn-Jeffreys, 48
muriatic acid, 133

natural gas, 72, 111
neon, 151; abundance of, 68, 77;
    atomic number of, 50; boiling
    point of, 104; discovery of, 40;
    electron distribution of, 66; ioni-
    zation potential of, 125; isotopes
    of, 52–53; lifting power of, 94–
    95; melting point of, 106; nuclear
    structure of, 60; solubility of, 99;
    symbol of, 52; total supply of, 80;
    uses of, 86–88
neon-21, 80–81
neon-24, 55
neon glow lamp, 86
neon lights, 86
Neptune, 69
neutrons, 57
Newton, Isaac, 11
nickel, 47
Nicklès, Jérôme, 135
niobium, 110
niobium-tin alloy, 112
nitrides, 84
nitrogen, 6–7; abundance of, 68;
    atomic, 23; atomic weight of, 19;
    boiling point of, 103; density of,
    19–26, 93; earth's atmosphere and,
    70; electronegativity of, 129; in-
    ertness of, 113; ionization poten-
    tial of, 125; light bulbs and, 83;
    liquefaction of, 38; melting point

of, 106; solubility of, 98; triatomic, 23, 33
nitrogen molecules, 22
nitrogen oxide, 125
Nobel Prizes, 41, 105, 137
noble gas(es), 10; abundance of, 77–81; atomic numbers of, 50; boiling points of, 104; compounds of, 146–157; densities of, 92–93; discovery of, 26, 36–41; electron distributions of, 65–66; historic dates of, 162–164; inertness of, 113 ff., ionization potentials of, 124–125; melting point of, 105–106; nuclear structure of, 60; solubilities of, 98–99; symbols of, 52; total supply of, 80; uses of, 82 ff.
noble gas compounds, 146 ff.; uses of, 154–157; valence and, 160
noble gas hydrates, 115–117
nucleons, 57
nucleus, atomic, 48; structure of, 57–59

osmium, 145 n.
osmium hexafluoride, 145
oxides, 84
oxidizing agents, 156–157
oxygen, 6–7; abundance of, 68; atmosphere and, 70; atomic weight of, 19; boiling point of, 102–103; density of, 19, 93; electron distribution in, 63; electronegativity of, 129; fluorine and, 137–139; ionization potential of, 127; isotopes of, 141; liquefaction of, 38; melting point of, 106; solubility of, 98; xenon and, 151–153
oxygen family, 63
oxygen fluoride, 138
oxygen molecules, 22; ionization potential of, 127
ozone, 22, 135

palladium, 145 n.
particles, subatomic, 48
Pauling, Linus, 129, 131, 134, 139, 160
periodic table, 29, 44–45; atomic number and, 47–50; electron distribution and, 64; noble gases and, 33–35, 41, 45–46
petroleum, 72
phlogiston, 6
phosphorus, 136
platinum, 135–136, 145–146
platinum hexafluoride, 146
plutonium, 157
polonium, 44
potassium, 58, 65, 123, 134; isotopes of, 56–57
potassium-40, 57, 75–76
potassium hydrogen fluoride, 135
Priestley, Joseph, 4
protons, 57
Prout, William, 17
Prout's hypothesis, 17, 59

quartz, 142 n., 152

radioactivity, 43
radium, 44, 63, 90
radium emanation, 45
radon, 51; abundance of, 68, 77, 81; atomic number of, 50; boiling point of, 104; compounds of, 147, 150; density of, 93; discovery of, 45; electron distribution of, 66; formation of, 79; inertness of, 114; ionization potential of, 125; isotopes of, 56; melting point of, 106; nuclear structure of, 60; solubility of, 99; symbol of, 52 n.; uses of, 90
radon-222, 56
radon hydrate, 115
Ramsay, William, 25, 35, 41, 45, 72, 86, 113

Rayleigh, Lord, 18, 35, 41, 61, 113
Reich, Ferdinand, 13
rhodium, 145 n.
rhodium hexafluoride, 146
Richter, Hieronymos T., 13
rockets, 144
rocks, age of, 76–77
rubidium, 13, 65, 123
ruthenium, 145 n.
ruthenium hexafluoride, 146
Rutherford, Daniel, 5
Rutherford, Ernest, 48, 57, 72

sand, 142 n.
Saturn, 69
Scheele, Karl W., 132
Schwanhard, Heinrich, 132
second sound, 108
selenium, 63
Selig, Henry, 147
serendipity, 16 n.
shielded arc-welding, 84
silicon, 85, 142; abundance of, 68
silicon dioxide, 142, 152
silicon tetrafluoride, 143, 152
silver, 109
Soddy, Frederick, 51
sodium, 134; electron distribution of, 65; ionization potential of, 120–121, 123
sodium perxenate, 153
sodium vapor lamp, 86
solar wind, 74
solid state, 100
sound waves, 99
spark chamber, 87
spectroscopic analysis, 12
spectrum, light, 11
spontaneous fission, 78
strontium, 63, 134
Strutt, John W., 18
sulfur, 48, 63, 129
sun, 13, 68–69
superconductivity, 109

superfluidity, 107

tantalum, 83, 101, 110
technetium, 109
tellurium, 34, 63
temperature, absolute, 102
thallium, 13
Thomson, Joseph J., 51
Thomson, William, 102
thorium, 43, 55, 72
thorium emanation, 45
thoron, 45, 51
titanium, 85
tralphium, 73–74
transistors, 85
Travers, William M., 37, 86
tritium, 73
tungsten, 83, 101

universe, elements of, 67–68
Urey, Harold C., 68
uraninite, 15
uranium, 43; atomic structure of, 48; fission of, 78; isotopes of, 140–143
uranium-235, 55, 140
uranium-238, 55, 140; helium formation and, 72
uranium dioxide, 141
uranium hexafluoride, 143
uranium oxide, 141
uranium tetrafluoride, 143
Uranus, 69

valence, 29, 117; electron distribution and, 63–64; noble gas compounds and, 160
Van Helmont, Jan B., 3, 8
vapor lamp, 85–86
Villard, P., 115

Walpole, Horace, 16 n.
water, 102; earth's atmosphere and, 70–71; xenon fluorides and, 152
water vapor, 93

xenic acid, 153
xenon, 40–41; abundance of, 68, 77,
80; atomic number of, 50; boiling point of, 104; compounds of,
146–157; density of, 93; electron
distribution of, 66; fluorine and,
147–150; formation of, 79; inertness of, 114 n.; ionization potential of, 125; isotopes of, 54; melting point of, 106; nuclear structure
of, 60; oxygen and, 151–153; solubility of, 99; symbol of, 52 n.;
uses of, 89–90
xenon-126, 80–81
xenon-127, 55
xenon compounds, 146 ff.; water
and, 152; uses of, 154–157
xenon difluoride, 149

xenon hexafluoride, 149, 152
xenon hydrate, 115
xenon nitrate, 153
xenon oxytetrafluoride, 152
xenon platinofluoride, 146
xenon rhodiofluoride, 146–147
xenon rutheniofluoride, 147
xenon tetrafluoride, 148–149
xenon trioxide, 152–153, 156
xenon vapor lamp, 90
X-rays, 89

Yost, Don M. L., 139, 146, 159
Yukawa, Hideki, 75

Zeppelin, Count Ferdinand von, 93
zero-point energy, 106